RELEASE FROM
FROM
TENSION

RELEASE FROM TENSION

by

Paul E. Adolph, M.D., M.Sc. (Med.), F.A.C.S.

MOODY PRESS
CHICAGO

FOREWORD

by

Robert A. Cook,

Today's physician is often expected not only to diagnose our ailments, but to agree tactfully with our ideas as to what causes them, as well. All too often, we reserve the right to be totally and belligerently blind to the real villains in the case — our inner resentments, tensions, and fears.

Through the years, Dr. Paul Adolph has displayed the erudition and ability that make him trusted and appreciated as a doctor, coupled with the kindly common sense that brings these medical mysteries within grateful reach of the average layman.

Not only so, but he brings to his work the conviction that there is an answer in Christ — Christ in the life of the believer — for every problem we will ever face. This man is beloved by many because in the process of helping them to feel better, he caused them to face their real problems — and solve them — with Christ.

This book will be read . . . because it is highly interesting. It is hoped that many as they read will pray over these pages with the heartfelt question, "Lord, is it I? Art Thou trying to teach me something here? Help me to listen — and to obey!"

INTRODUCTION

by

M. R. De Haan, M.D.

THIS TIMELY VOLUME on the release from tensions, by Dr. Paul E. Adolph, fills an urgent and long-felt need. A book on this subject, written from the standpoint of a Christian physician, has long been overdue. In the last few years I have often felt the urge to write something on this much-neglected subject from the Bible standpoint. But the urge never materialized, and after reading Dr. Adolph's manuscript, I knew the reason why. The Lord had someone else to do the job better than I could possibly have done, and I feel deeply honored in having even the small part of writing an introduction to the excellent and scriptural approach to this up-to-date problem.

Science has recognized the close association of the mind and body, and is beginning to realize how much of our physical symptoms are only symptoms of a mental condition. Correction of these real or imaginary inhibitions and frustrations often results in a complete disappearance of all physical manifestations.

The sects and the cults and the quacks have been quick to recognize the possibilities open to them. Utilizing the power of suggestion, diversion, and even hypnotism, they have created a veritable racket. This is merely a mental relief, a psychic narcosis without lasting peace of heart.

How often we have witnessed the dramatic relief afforded people who went to someone to unburden themselves to "get it off their chest!" I have had folk come to my office in the night, and being assured that no one could hear, they would pour out their tale of sorrow. "Oh, doctor, I just had to go to someone. This thing in my life is driving me crazy," and then they would pour out their hearts, sometimes confessing the most gruesome things. I have learned to always let them talk and not interfere. I never interrupt them until they are through, and then invariably they will say something like this, "Well, thank the Lord, I feel better now. I've got it off my chest." And yet I had not done one single thing except simply listen.

There can be no permanent release from all these ills except by a recognition of the scriptural and spiritual answer to the question of perfect inner peace. As Dr. Adolph has so thoroughly set forth in one of his chapters, man must get into proper relation to God through a new birth by faith in Jesus Christ the Son of God, and then and then only can he approach the High Priest of our salvation and find the peace *of* God which passeth understanding. First there must be peace *with* God through the new birth, and then only is the peace *of* God possible to those who utilize the offices of our High Priest who lives to listen to our confessions and releases us from our tensions.

The way is given in I John 1:9: "If we confess our sins, he is faithful and just to forgive us our sins, and to cleanse us from all unrighteousness."

The healing in James 5 is also made conditional upon confession, and Paul tells us in Philippians 4:6, 7: "Be careful for nothing; but in everything by prayer and supplication with thanksgiving let your requests be made known unto God. And the peace of God, which passeth all understanding, shall keep your hearts and minds through Christ Jesus." Here is the divine prescription for lasting peace.

With a fervent prayer for a wide circulation of this volume among God's people, I recommend it heartily, as filling a most timely need in this world of neurotics and psychotics who need the real remedy for peace and freedom from care — personal saving faith in the finished work and the shed blood, and the resurrection of the Lord Jesus Christ.

CONTENTS

RELEASE
FROM
TENSION

Chapter 1

THE RELATION OF EMOTIONAL STATE TO BODILY HEALTH

Beloved, I wish above all things that thou mayest prosper and be in health, even as thy soul prospereth. — III John 2

THIS BOOK is being written because it appears that our large American cities in the present era of hurry and rush are experiencing more diminution in working capacity from emotional tensions and maladjustments than is warranted, particularly when the potentialities of Christianity are considered. It is the author's conviction on the basis of experience that Christianity, conscientiously applied to the emotional tension problems of our era, offers complete and satisfactory solution, not only to these tensions, but also to the disease symptoms which they so often produce.

It is not our purpose to offer a compendium for diagnosis of ills resulting from emotional tensions. Actually the differences between these ills and others of an organic type usually require the diagnostic acumen of the expert. However, it is not deemed essential that definite diagnosis be made by the layman. All that is needed is (1) an awareness that these ills do exist as a result of emotional maladjustments; and (2) a resolve on the part of the individual concerned to deal with his problem on a spiritual Christian plane in a complete and uncompromising manner. Whether or not the emotional tensions are already producing disease symptoms is beside the point. The fact that they can and may should be adequate incentive to set our spiritual house in order. Even without this incentive we owe it to ourselves that it be done.

The mid-twentieth century has seen a reemphasis of things which concern the mind and spirit in contrast to the crass materialism which prevailed in the nineteenth century. We have, as it were, rediscovered that man is not a mere machine, composed of just atoms and molecules. Psychology and psychiatry, with all due apologies for their failings, have come to the place where stress is given to the fact that we are something more than just material substance and that our thought-life is not the simple outcome of chemical reactions between the chemical compounds contained therein.

The discovery of bacterial microorganisms, visible to the human eye as the material cause of disease through the use of the microscope, was no small factor in focusing attention upon material causation of disease. It was perhaps naturally assumed that all disease was caused by bacteria or by similar microorganisms. It is true that this did cast into oblivion many of the superstitions which had preceded these observations. However, it did mean that other factors were lost sight of which are active in causing diseases. These factors and these diseases are no less real than bacteria and the diseases caused by them. Indeed, so thoroughly has the average layman of today become versed in this materialistic and mechanistic attitude that he often thinks that when causes of disease, such as emotional tensions and maladjustments, are referred to, he is being accused of imagining his symptoms and of having an imaginary ailment.

The fact is that we are not merely an accretion of atoms and molecules. We are people with mental and emotional reactions, and it is largely this that distinguishes us from the mineral, vegetable, and animal world about us. We can rejoice that this distinction exists. It gives us what we call personality. Moreover, we must realize that healthy personality adjustments are even more important than the avoidance of the bacteria round about, important as that is. In other words, a great number of serious disease states, which are not caused by bacteria, and which are not of an imaginary nature but of tangible and real character, are ready to attack us. Their cause is not imaginary either but is as visible as bacteria are under the microscope through the utilization of just ordinary insight. How blind some of us have allowed ourselves to be through closing our eyes to these realities!

It is our purpose here to discuss what information ordinary insight gives us in regard to some of the diseases whose cause is to be found in emotional tensions and personality maladjustments and to correlate them (1) with the facts of anatomy, physiology, and pathology; and (2) with divine revelation as given to us through the Bible. No apology is made for doing so, although we realize that medical science is in measure a changing science as new discoveries are made year by year. We merely assume that the great bulk of these scientific data are substantially reliable. Similarly, we do not attempt to go into theological apologetics to establish our reason for belief in the Bible. It appeals to us as fulfilling the requirements of a workable knowledge of God and relationships to Him and to our fellow men. Some of the evidence for the latter will be discussed in chapter **3.**

That disease symptoms on an emotional basis are frequently encountered in present-day medical practice is abundantly evident. It is conservatively estimated that over fifty percent of the patients who come to the general practitioner's office in our large cities have no demonstrable organic disease. They are, nevertheless, suffering real disease symptoms on an emotional tension basis. No doubt the tempo at which we live is a factor in this but most likely this operates by reason of the fact that in our speed of living we bypass many unresolved emotional situations only to meet them head-on at a later time.

From a study of anatomy it is clear that there is an intricate system of conductive fibers called nerves which serve largely through the intermediation of the brain to integrate the various organs of the body. These nerves carry impulses by a mechanism similar to that by which electric wires carry electrical impulses. The proper function of the nerves is dependent in great measure upon the balancing of the load which is placed upon them just as is the case with an electrical system. When an overload of one of the lines of the electrical system of an ordinary house is encountered, such as is produced through plugging into the same line two heavy users of electricity such as an electric heater and an electric waffle iron, the outcome may well be the burning out of the fuse. Sim-

ilarly, when the nervous system, which inter-
mediates emotional and sensory impulses of the
human body, becomes overloaded, a fuse has to
give way as it were, or at least the superabund-
ant nervous impulses must be sidetracked.
These accumulate as bodily manifestations of
disturbed emotional patterns, usually referable
to emotional tensions.

These emotional patterns are somewhat di-
versified but the symptom patterns are as rec-
ognizable by the experienced physician as the
symptom patterns of pneumonia or appendici-
tis. While in any case the diagnosis cannot be
made definite without confirmatory physical
examination and laboratory findings, the defi-
niteness of these emotional patterns cannot be
denied. At the risk of being guilty of oversimplification, we are listing three of the most common symptom patterns, not with the idea of
affording a diagnosis for those suffering from
emotional tensions, for diagnosis is not as simple as that, but in order that there may be some
comprehension as to the type of symptoms produced. If overloading of the nervous system
can be recognized early and corrected, there is
hope that the burned-out fuses, as it were, and
the accumulation of emotional tensions, can be
prevented before deep ruts are worn in the
road to permanent damage.

Three of the more common tension patterns
suggest themselves for mention which for con-

venience we may name: (1) the stiff-neck tension pattern; (2) the chest tension pattern; and (3) the stomach tension pattern.

The *stiff-neck tension pattern* is characterized by painfully contracted muscles in the back of the neck. From here the pain may extend upward to the top of the head and the forehead, in the form of headache, downward into the so-called trapezius muscles which are located above and between the shoulder blades, and/or forward to produce a tense feeling in the throat. Often it appears that this muscular tension is an attempt at compensation for *lack of backbone* in dealing with seemingly overwhelming problems. The person becomes tense and apprehensive and often there is sleep disturbance. Paradoxically, this, which may have started as a manifestation of a lack of backbone, may eventually lead to a stubborn, unbending attitude such as characterized the Israelites under Moses when they were called a stiff-necked people. For this reason, these sufferers often become especially hard to help because they cannot see their way clear into accepting the explanation of their symptom pattern, nor can they readily alter their ways once the pattern becomes firmly established.

The *chest tension pattern* consists of complaints referable to the chest such as conscious (and sometimes rapid) beating of the heart, discomfort over the heart region which may

even be described as pain, a sense of squeezing
of the chest as in a vise, and sighing breathing
even when no exertion factors have preceded
it. Physiologists point out that this is largely
due to an imbalance of the nerves of the heart,
the nerves which put the brakes on the heart
being understimulated and the nerves which
speed the heart being overstimulated. Perhaps
the term *losing heart* best expresses this, for the
heart is running away with itself, as it were, as
the driver's foot presses more and more firmly
on the accelerator. Once the driver's foot is
transferred from the accelerator to the brake, almost instantaneous relief follows. These sufferers are often fairly easily relieved of their
complaints, once the nature of their source is
pointed out, even though up to this time the
patient is quite convinced that he has organic
heart trouble. This relief is often accomplished
by the resolution of an anxiety through getting
it "off the chest."

The *stomach tension pattern,* often referred
to as nervous indigestion, is characterized by a
feeling of bloat after eating, a sensation of in-
ward tension in the abdomen frequently described as "butterflies" and sometimes a vague
feeling of nausea. These symptoms correspond
to what happens when the stomach is filled beyond its functional capacity. Interestingly
enough these symptoms are produced in the
stomach when the emotions reach a state and

type of tension such as is described by the term *fed-up*.[1] Often emotional tensions which affect the stomach are those of resentfulness and bitterness. These tensions may at times be rather tenacious. On the other hand, very frequently temporary relief of symptoms at least is obtained through medicines which tend to reestablish the nervous balance of the stomach. If permanent relief is to be obtained, it usually is necessary to deal with the resentful and unforgiving spirit. Otherwise peptic ulcer may eventually result in some cases.

Admittedly, the above description of tension patterns is an oversimplification. These patterns may coexist or may change from one into the other. There are also other possible tension patterns, for instance those involving the skin, the lower bowel (colon), or the bladder. Our purpose in describing the tension patterns has been largely to emphasize that there must be forthright dealing with the causes of the emotional tensions. Otherwise disease symptoms may continue to impair health and be conducive to the contracting of even more serious disease.

Since emotional state is largely a matter of the condition of the soul and spirit, it is our conviction that further discussion of these matters is useless apart from dealing directly with the

---

[1]Other emotional situations affecting the stomach are also recognized corresponding to the empty stomach with its hunger contractions and accompanying irritating secretions, attributed to *underfed* frustrations.

origin and growth of spiritual life. In the next chapter therefore we discuss the matter of the new birth which comprises, as we see it, the beginning of genuine spiritual life. We consider this most important for we are convinced that, if there is genuine spiritual life with continuous growth therein through the transforming power of the Holy Spirit, instead of world conformity, there need not be the degree of ill health among so-called Christian people that is commonly observed today.

Chapter 2

THE OBSTETRICS OF THE NEW BIRTH

That which is born of the flesh is flesh, and that which is born of the Spirit is spirit. — JOHN 3:6

WHEN A BABY IS BORN, the acts of four persons are of importance. (1) The mother has to experience *travail* or labor of variable duration and severity. (2) The baby must *cry*. (3) The physician must effect by approved technique the *separation* of the baby from the mother and duly certify thereto. (4) The father or other observers usually come along and *substantiate*, whether through the glass window of the nursery or more intimately, the unmistakable signs of a new life, perhaps in a naïve grimace of the face, or maybe in ungainly motion of the fingers, toes, arms, and legs. These procedures are those which we associate with the birth of a baby. The art and science of obstetrics are concerned with these matters.

Our Lord Jesus Christ, when here on earth, commonly used the simple facts and experiences of ordinary life as illustrations to clarify spiritual truths. Some of these illustrations were in the form of parables where the matter of likeness was to be stressed in just certain respects. In some other instances the matter of similitude was so close that a direct metaphor was employed, saying in effect, "This *is* that." Such would seem to be the case in His discourse concerning the new birth with Nicodemus, one of the rulers of the Jews, as recorded in the third chapter of the Gospel of John.

In this discourse Jesus so closely compared the spiritual new birth with physical birth that even learned Nicodemus was momentarily mystified and asked: "How can a man be born when he is old? Can he enter the second time into his mother's womb, and be born?" (John 3:4).

In reply to this query Jesus pointed out the sharp distinction between physical life and spiritual life when He said: "That which is born of the flesh is flesh, and that which is born of the Spirit is spirit" (John 3:6). Two basic biological concepts are included in this statement: (1) like begets like; and (2) life is produced only from pre-existing life (and not from spontaneous generation).

There is no vagueness in Jesus' metaphor such as some want to interject into theological concepts nowadays. The spiritual new birth is clearly the *sine qua non* of the Christian life, just as the physical birth is of physical life. It cannot be a halfway measure, any more than a baby can be half born. It must be a definite and complete transaction.

When one is born again, moreover, it must be of spiritual parentage, even of the Spirit of God, who is also known as the Holy Spirit, the third Person of the Godhead. Furthermore, just as the mother accomplishes the birth of her baby as the outcome of travail or labor, frequently with great pain and suffering, even so our Lord Jesus accomplished the basis of our spiritual birth at the expense of great suffering on Calvary's cross. It was there, as He shed His blood for us, that our redemption was completed, as attested by our Lord's words on the cross, "It is finished" (John 19:30). It was with this in view that the prophet Isaiah exclaimed: "He shall see of the travail of his soul and shall be satisfied" (Isa. 53:11).

However, even though the travail and suffering is accomplished, there is no new life until the individual concerned, helpless though he or she be, does one thing which is really so simple that it hardly seems like doing anything at all. That one thing is to cry. It is *the cry* of the infant that makes the difference between death (the so-called stillbirth) and new life, as the newborn babe inflates its lungs by taking its first breath of air. Indeed, it is the height of disappointment to witness all the suffering, travail, and mental planning on the part of the mother, only to find that no cry is put forth by the infant such as to produce life as a new individual.

How much more is this true spiritually! We in our weakness can actually do nothing to obtain the life of the Spirit, which is our salvation, nor can we add anything to that which has been already done by our Lord and Saviour Jesus Christ. The apostle Paul gave expression to this when he said: "For when we were yet without strength, in due time Christ died for the ungodly" (Rom. 5:6). Moreover, he adds that it is "not by works done in righteousness, which we did ourselves, but according to his mercy he saved us, through the washing of regeneration, and renewing of the Holy Spirit" (Titus 3:5, A.S.V.). Thus it is for us in our utter helplessness to receive Christ's finished work as applied to us through the cry of simple faith unto God. In this way the entrance of the life of the Spirit is accomplished: "For whosoever shall call upon the name of the Lord shall be saved" (Rom. 10:13).

The Spirit of God broods and yearns over us, waiting for that response in the form of a simple cry on our part that means the difference between life and no life. David of old was finding salvation through such a cry when he exclaimed: "I will cry unto God most high; unto God that performeth all things for me. He shall send from heaven, and save me" (Ps. 57:2, 3).

Perhaps few realize all the implications of. the physician's care at the time of birth. Apart from the actual measures taken to alleviate pain, to prevent infectious processes, and to secure unobstructed, safe delivery of the baby (and the author's contacts with situations where such care was lacking during his nearly 15 years in China convinces him of their paramount importance), the physician stands in a strategic semi-official relationship to the local government. It is he that certifies as to the place and time of the birth in such a way as to establish more or less permanently the nationality of the newborn individual and his future relationship to that nation, such as in selective service and old-age pension plans. In Jesus' conversation with Nicodemus, this very matter of nationality was discussed with reference to the spiritual realm. He definitely established the nationality of those who are born of the Spirit as being that of native-born citizens of the kingdom of God. His references to inability to see or to enter this kingdom apart from being born of the Spirit are very pertinent indeed.

The barrier between the life of the body, which belongs to the animal kingdom, and the life of the Spirit, which belongs to the kingdom

of God, may be compared with the barrier between the mineral kingdom and the animal
kingdom. Neither of these barriers can be
crossed by any other means than through birth.
We know much about the chemical elements
and chemical compounds which constitute the
framework of the human body, but gathering
these substances together in their proper pro-
portions does not in any wise give us animal
life. Entrance into the animal kingdom is only
effected by physical birth from pre-existing animal life. So also we may gather together many
elements, which we recognize as characteristic
of the life of the Spirit, but this does not give
us the life of the Spirit. Entrance into the kingdom of God is only effected by spiritual birth
from the pre-existing life of the Spirit which
God alone can impart.

Let us further illustrate this point. As an
American medical missionary, seeking entry
into China years ago, I could not but be impressed by the hundreds of millions of Chinese
who had entered China with no difficulty whatsoever and were reckoned as citizens of China
by just being born there. I for my part was
limited in my entry into that land by having to
come under constant surveillance wherever I
went. Indeed, even my passport was at times
called into question and was valid for only
limited periods at a time. Permanent entry into
China had been accomplished with ease by

those who were born there of Chinese parents. Even so, the true entry into the kingdom of God is only to be achieved by those who are born there, that is, begotten of the Spirit of God, and who have acquired the characteristics of the citizens of the kingdom of God through birth.

Furthermore, in my missionary work in China I at first thought that I could be much more successful in the work by identifying myself with the Chinese. I applied myself to learning the reading, writing, and speaking of the Chinese language. I studied the Chinese classics. I learned to eat Chinese food with chopsticks. Living in the interior of China, I wore Chinese clothes. While this all added tremendously to my efficiency in the work, yet try as I might, I was not truly identified with the Chinese people, for my nationality remained perfectly obvious as being American. My entry into China was on a temporary basis. My nationality was American because I had been born of American parents as attested by my passport, my accent in speaking, and my general demeanor.

The same is even truer in the spiritual realm where even temporary entry to a noncitizen is denied. Our Lord Jesus made the matter very clear that it is impossible to enter or even see the spiritual realm, the kingdom of God, apart from being born anew of the Spirit of God (John 3:3, 5).

It is to be noted that two terms are used in connection with an individual's relationship to the kingdom of God, namely: (1) see, and (2) enter. Some folk seem to think that even though they cannot enter into all the rights and privileges of citizenship in the kingdom of God because they have not taken the step of faith involved in crying unto God, they can at least see for themselves the things of the kingdom of God and then make up their minds as to whether they want to enter or not. Jesus, however, pointed out that it is not even possible to catch a proper glimpse of the kingdom of God without the spiritual insight that comes from being born anew. This is further stressed by the apostle Paul when he says: "Eye hath not seen, nor ear heard, neither have entered into the heart of man, the things which God hath prepared for them that love him. But God hath revealed them to us by his Spirit" (I Cor. 2:9, 10).

This lack of insight in matters outside the realm of personal experience was forcibly impressed upon me when I was formerly trying to explain to a Chinese patient uninitiated into the realm of the microscopic, that he had doubtless gotten some germs into his flesh wound. The patient contradicted my explanation with an air of finality, for he said he himself had looked at the wound at frequent intervals and he knew there were absolutely no germs there!

We also find that the nationals of a country are usually the only ones who really have true insight into the affairs of their own people. Other folk may come to live among them, eating their food, speaking their language, and wearing their clothes, but there is usually a lack of full insight into the customs and thinking of that nation unless one has been born of parents of that nationality.

In like manner intellectual uplift, rationalization, and pious phrases, good as they are, can never bring the individual to the state of being spiritually enlightened apart from being born of the Spirit of God. Environmental influences can never lift us from the realm of the physical into the realm of the spiritual. We cannot lift ourselves into Heaven by pulling ourselves up by our own bootstraps. Like begets like, and it is only by being born of the Spirit of God that we obtain the life of the Spirit. We cannot expect spontaneous generation of spiritual life from physical life. It is contrary to all the processes of nature and to the teachings of the Bible as well. Jesus said: "Marvel not that I said unto thee, Ye must be born again" (John 3:7).

There simply is no other way to see or to enter the kingdom of God and become a citizen of Heaven than to believe on the Lord Jesus Christ as Saviour and thus become born anew.

"For God so loved the world, that he gave his only begotten Son, that whosoever *believeth* in him should not perish, but have *everlasting life*" (John 3:16). It is then that we can say: "Our citizenship is in heaven; whence also we wait for a Saviour, the Lord Jesus Christ" (Phil. 3:20, 21, A.S.V.).

But the skeptic may ask, "Where is the evidence for all this? I do not believe. Therefore I cannot see or enter the kingdom of God. How can I know that this new life is possible?"

Jesus answered this objection very concisely when He pointed to the clues that there was wind round about Him. Of course, no one could see the wind. Moreover, the moment one attempts to grasp hold of a piece of it in one's hand to examine it, it ceases to be wind. Nevertheless, there was unmistakable evidence all around that there was wind blowing, for as it blew it produced sound (John 3:8) and also doubtless was causing visible motion of the leaves and branches of the trees.

Similarly, as the observer looks at the signs of new life in the infant, it is not by dissecting apart that infant body that the presence of life is confirmed, for as soon as we endeavor to hold up to view that evanescent something called life in a dissecting forceps, it ceases to be life! Actually the true clues of life are observed by that overjoyed father as he sees the grimaces, the yawns, the at first meaningless and purposeless gesticulations of the infant, and hears its cry. He is convinced beyond all doubt that life is there.

Even so is it in connection with the life of the Spirit. When a new nature shows itself so that there is love where formerly there was hate; there is sweetness where formerly there was bitterness; there is peace where formerly there was worry, fretting, and anxiety; there is joy and hope where formerly there was unhappiness and desperation; and there is patience where formerly there was impatience — then we may say that here the life of the Spirit is manifested. This is genuine evidence.

Birth is the way a new life comes into the world physically, and birth is the way new life comes into the world spiritually. Let it not be supposed, however, that this is the end. Actually, the infant child is of importance because of the potentialities which are reached after a prolonged period of growth. Nothing is perhaps more pitiable than an infant who does not go on to grow.

The same is true of the spiritual life. It must not be thought that spiritual maturity is attained in any sense by the first cry. Actually there are many more cries to be anticipated. We must go on trusting our Saviour day by day. Growth takes place only as one feeds daily upon the spiritual nourishment provided in God's Word. There follows a prolonged period of growth under the chastening and disciplining hand of God, "till we all come in the unity of the faith, and of the knowledge of the Son of God, unto a perfect man, unto the measure of the stature of the fullness of Christ: that we henceforth be no more children, tossed to and fro" (Eph. 4:13, 14).

First, we must recognize that spiritual life has not begun until we cry unto God in simple faith. Then, those of us who have taken this step must give heed to the scriptural injunction: "Let us go on unto perfection . . . and things that accompany salvation" (Heb. 6:1, 9).

Chapter 3

THE REASONABLENESS
OF FAITH

*I am not ashamed of the gospel of Christ: for
it is the power of God unto salvation to everyone that believeth . . . for therein is the righteousness of God revealed from faith to faith.*
— ROMANS 1:16, 17

FROM THE FOREGOING DISCUSSION it is obvious
that faith in God and His Word plays a most
important part in our entering and advancing
in a truly spiritual life. It therefore is appropriate that we digress a bit to show how reasonable it is for us to rely upon this faith.

It is of our weaknesses that we are ashamed.
There is no cause for our being ashamed when
power and strength are ours. On this basis the
apostle Paul said in Romans 1:16, 17: "I am not
ashamed of the gospel of Christ: for it is the
power of God unto salvation to everyone that

believeth . . . for therein is the righteousness of God revealed from faith to faith." It was reasonable for the apostle to be unashamed of that which was proving to be the inner power of his life through faith.

It is not our purpose here to prove from extraneous sources the uniqueness and indispensability of this power and the faith wherein it lies, but rather to examine directly this faith in Christ and to discern wherein it appears to be reasonable and worth while.

The apostle tells us that this power is "revealed *from* faith *to* faith." Obviously he does not mean that one goes traveling about in an endless circle from a point on the circle called faith back to the same point. Rather it would appear that we proceed from a small faith, which is characterized perchance by a degree of spontaneity without a full realization of all of faith's implications, to advance into a broader and larger sphere of faith. This small faith, starting in our heavenly Father's revelation of Himself in His Word, the Bible, eventually grows through exercise into a greater faith, which, while still based upon the same divine revelation, becomes integrated and rationalized into our thinking and activities. This greater faith is one with greater vistas and greater triumphs while all the time proving more and more reasonable through its demonstration of effectiveness.

To illustrate this, we may point to the fact that an infant at first almost instinctively in simple faith satisfies his hunger from the nourishment provided by his mother's breasts. He realizes his need is met. The way is prepared for the exercise of a larger faith based upon the fact that the parent evidently knows what is best for him. Thus, as other forms of food are offered to him, he learns to eat a greater variety of foods through the exercise of an ever-increasing faith.

There is one school of thought which would deprive us of all spiritual food until we have actually analyzed it by chemical analysis, as it were, to detect what nourishing elements are present so as to make an intelligent decision as to which foods we are going to utilize. The absurdity of this becomes immediately evident when we apply this thinking to the physical realm. Thus, our food chemist no doubt would long ago have starved to death in utter weakness if as a child he had insisted upon first proving in this fashion the value of foods in the test tube before he would partake of any.

Actually, the food chemist first learned the value of food nutrients as a child by heeding the suggestion to eat that which was set before him by a parent who was wiser and more experienced than he was. Most of what he does now is confirmatory by way of showing the reasonableness of what he learned from that exper-

ience based upon faith. His wider vista of
chemical knowledge is, moreover, based upon
an expanded faith founded upon certain im-
mutable chemical principles upon which he has
found he can rely.

Even thus, we too learn that the satisfaction
of our soul's hunger lies in childlike acceptance
of that which has been offered us in God's revelation to us, the Bible. This is in accord with
the words of our Lord Jesus when He said:
"Except ye be converted, and become *as little
children,* ye shall not enter into the kingdom
of heaven" (Matt. 18:3).

This childlike acceptance of God's Word is
that to which the apostle Paul alluded when he
observed: *"Faith cometh* by hearing, and hearing *by the word of God"* (Rom. 10:17). The
Bible is God's chosen vehicle of revelation of
Himself. It is true that He has partially revealed
Himself in nature as well. However, we do not
find out God through this revelation in nature
any more than does the child fully understand
his parent by merely examining the articles of
furniture and appointments about the home
which his devoted parent has placed there, even
though they may have been made by the father's own loving hands. Something more is
needed to reveal the father, and that is personal contact.

This is pre-eminently true of our heavenly
Father. He has not only revealed Himself in

nature. He has revealed Himself: (1) through His Son, the Lord Jesus Christ (Heb. 1:2), as He contacted mankind on this earth in human form and now contacts us by His Spirit; (2) through the written Word, the Bible, which speaks of Him. It is a matter of our letting this revelation of God in Jesus Christ enter our hearts through faith by giving heed to His Word. In this connection we do well to hearken to the command of our Lord Jesus to "take heed *what* ye hear" (Mark 4:24), lest we confuse the many competing voices of the world with this clear revelation of Himself.

We remain blind to divine truth until God reveals it to us by His Spirit as we by faith partake of those things which have been revealed to us. God's Word tells us: "Eye hath not seen, nor ear heard, neither have entered into the heart of man, the things which God hath prepared for them that love him. But God hath revealed them unto us by his Spirit. For . . . the things of God knoweth no man, but the Spirit of God" (I Cor. 2:9-11).

Well does the psalmist exhort us: "O taste and see that the Lord is good: blessed is the man that trusteth in him" (Ps. 34:8). It is by faith that the child tastes his food to the end that physical growth may ensue. So by faith we taste and partake of the Lord's goodness as revealed to us in His Word, and spiritual growth almost inevitably follows. No amount of physical or intellectual effort can compensate for this simple act of faith, but when this step is taken, it proves to be the most logical and reasonable thing in all the world!

There is scarcely anything in life that does not require the acceptance by faith of certain initial concepts. For instance, one performs the intellectual process of reasoning on the basis of the concept that he has a brain that can function in the process of reasoning and that it is trustworthy in the ideas that it produces. Nevertheless, scarcely anyone can say that he has subjected his own head to a proof which is directly tangible and visible to himself that there is actually a brain within his head. It therefore follows that even the most incredulous person, who says he only believes what he has seen with his physical eyes, must accept by faith the presence of a reliable functioning brain without tangible proof other than the pragmatic argument that there seems to be some sort of thinking mechanism at work which presumably is a brain.

Obviously the eye of faith is an avenue for obtaining evidence which is beyond the physical eye's perception. The desire to eliminate the use of the eye of faith, beyond its application to a few basic concepts such as the presence of a brain within the head, is unfortunately present in many. Actually, if the eye of faith which tells me that I have a brain can be relied upon for giving evidence of this fact, it can be used just as scientifically and consistently in gaining basic knowledge and experience in the spiritual realm. Consequently, the truly scientific point of view acknowledges that just as the presence of a reliable functioning brain must be accepted by faith for gaining evidence of things in the intellectual realm, it is reasonable that faith be exercised to gain evidence of things in the spiritual realm.

On the contrary, many in these days imply that they think they can proceed by natural intellectual processes without the eye of faith from reason to faith, i.e., from the intellectual realm into the spiritual realm. This, however, is inconsistent with the laws of nature. We do not see the lesser realm of the mineral kingdom proceeding by natural progress (which would be by spontaneous generation) into the higher realm of the animal kingdom, although processes are observed to transpire within an animal's body by degression whereby that which was once an integral part of the living organism (belonging to the animal kingdom) is changed into inert chemical substance (belonging to the mineral kingdom). Even so, spiritual life, which belongs to the higher spiritual realm, although it does exert influence upon and manifests itself within the lesser physical and intellectual realms, does not grow out of either the realm of the physical or the realm of the intellectual.

Spiritual matters have a spiritual beginning and a spiritual end. In other words they have a spiritual origin and do not find their origin in either the intellectual or physical realms, as clearly enunciated by our Lord when He said: "That which is born of the flesh is flesh; and that which is born of the Spirit is spirit" (John 3:6). At the same time this does not deny that spiritual matters also concern themselves with intellectual reasonings and physical activities, for faith is reasonable and those who have entered into its secrets have been enjoined to be "ready always to give an answer to every man that asketh . . . a reason of the hope" that is in them (I Peter 3:15).

To clarify our meaning we may draw an analogy from the relationship between the physical and intellectual realms. One does not acquire knowledge by physical processes unless these are accompanied from start to finish by intellectual processes. Laboratory work and pencil sketches, as used in modern education, all serve their purpose in impressing one's mind. The actual process of learning, however, is an intellectual process from beginning to end, merely finding its avenue of expression in the physical realm, for laboratory work and pencil sketches do not produce knowledge in the mentally deficient. Mere physical incidents and experiences do not become knowledge save by the process of mental integration, and the intellectual process does not start until mental integration takes place. The same is true of the spiritual realm. This finds its beginnings in faith. It is true that faith reasons and that faith is also reasonable, but faith does not find its birth in rationality. There is no other road to take: we start from faith, "we walk by faith" (II Cor. 5:7), and our goal is faith triumphant. In other words we proceed *from* faith *by* faith *to* faith.

Those who, discarding revelation, try to build their own spiritual world by their own intellectual powers are really not very far removed from idolatry. Idolaters from ancient times have carved their ideas of spirits and gods out of wood, clay, metal, and stone. The only advance of which our modern world can boast is the substitution of gray-matter for gray marble. Such idols do have the advantage that they can be altered as the individual changes his views from year to year, and also that they are possibly not likely to be so great an encumbrance to posterity. But beyond this, the bold fact remains that it is merely idolatry in a new form, this idea of making one's own god as one goes along through life. What else can it be but idolatry if we do not start with faith in God's revelation of Himself to us?

The agnostic, in rejecting what may be known of God through the eyes of faith putting trust in God's revelation to us in His Word, fails to apply to the spiritual realm the experimental processes which he routinely applies to the realm of the physical and intellectual. In the ultimate, as pointed out before, knowledge in the physical and intellectual realms has come in great measure through the exercise of faith and the evidences for it are pragmatic, namely, that it makes sense in its workings.

As for the spiritual realm, it is on a higher plane than the intellectual, and it is preposterous to expect to attain to an understanding of the spiritual through merely laying hold of the possibly unstable products of the human intellect, particularly those of the mind of a man who starts with the premise that God is unknowable. God in His Word says: "For my thoughts are not your thoughts, neither are your ways my ways, saith the Lord, for as the heavens are higher than the earth, so are my ways higher than your ways, and my thoughts than your thoughts" (Isa. 55:8, 9). Logically, our reason for belief in the spiritual (or lack of such belief as the case may be) must be based upon the same type of direct and sincere experimentation and experience within the spiritual realm that we apply in any other realm.

Our approach to spiritual matters may be likened to that of the swimmer in deep water. In simple faith that the water will hold him up, he plunges in and swims about. As he comes out of the water, he perceives that the water effectively holds him up while he is swimming and that he is refreshed and invigorated. The whole procedure impresses him as reasonable despite the fact that he did not carry out the procedure, which at first might seem more logical, though really impracticable, of starting at the bottom and working his way up.

Unquestionably our outlook on life is influenced greatly by our explanation of how the world came into existence. The succinct statement of Hebrews 11:3 appeals to us as being the most comprehensible explanation: "Through faith we understand that the worlds were framed by the word of God, so that things which are seen were not made of things which do appear."

Men of all ages have sought for an explanation of the origins of things. Many hypotheses have been set up only to be superseded by what seemed to be better ones. Concerning the process by which things came into being, there are, to be sure, many details of which we are in ignorance; but as regards the essential element in the process we need not be in doubt, for by faith we understand that the first-cause in producing the world was God. No successful refutation of this has ever been made despite the fact that many hypotheses have been propounded in an effort to explain details. Often these hypotheses, indeed, have merely served to make one lose sight of the first-cause through the bewilderment of the mind over details.

For instance, we are told that there is an ancient folklore which explains that the earth is poised on the back of an elephant, and that the elephant is in turn standing on a tortoise. However, the explanation stops here with no explanation as to what the tortoise stands on. Therefore, even if it were true, the explanation explains nothing, and to all intents and purposes the earth remains unsupported in space. Such are all explanations of the origins of things which ignore the first-cause.

By some, "resident forces" have been proposed as the agent which brought the world into existence, but what the force was that started the resident forces into action (i.e., the first-cause) usually remains unexplained. This explanation is therefore no better than the folklore which takes us back to the tortoise.

Some hypotheses have supposed that things came into being by a process of chance mutation. These same people would, of course, explain the affairs of ordinary life as happening by chance, which many of us, who see with the eyes of faith, find hard to believe. The fact is that it would seem to be easier to explain God away from the ordinary affairs of life, if that can be done, than from the process of creation. If God is in the so-called chance affairs of the present, how can we explain Him away from the affairs of the past where our presuming mind was not present to lend its guiding voice? Indeed, the sum total of wisdom manifested in the creation of all things (Prov. 8:22-31) would seem to make the notion of the operation of chance in these matters preposterous.

Those who have made attempts at explaining the origin of things other than the explanation given in the Bible, we are told, have "changed the truth of God into a lie, and worshiped and served the creature more than the Creator, who is blessed forever" (Rom. 1:25). Merely distracting the mind from the first-cause of things does not explain their origin. The fact is that the first-cause remains a mystery until we stand on faith in God.

The very nature of things being what it is, how else could we understand the first-cause in creation except by faith in revelation? None of us was there to observe the process. Examination of the strata laid down in past geological ages to determine the nature of the first-cause is similar to a scrutiny of the carpenter's shavings to find out what the carpenter is like. Moreover, the study of nature in its present form may be likened to the study of the carpentry to determine the attributes of its maker. It is true that through nature study we have strong evidence of the power, thoroughness, and skill of the Maker of the universe (cf. Rom. 1:20), but as to His own character of love in redemption of a lost world, a personal acquaintance must be obtained through revelation. Indeed, it has been aptly intimated that a knowledge of the nature of the rocks and of the ages of the rocks cannot be advantageously substituted for a knowledge of the Rock of Ages such as is only acquired through faith in God's revelation of Himself.

The revelation of God's Word is the only direct evidence that we have of the character of the first-cause, and other attempts at bringing forth evidence, when this is rejected, are to be regarded as futile. So then it is *"through faith we understand"* (Heb. 11:3) and our hearts re-echo the words of praise of our Saviour when He said: "I thank thee, O Father, Lord of heaven and earth, because thou hast hid these things from the wise and prudent, and hast revealed them unto babes. Even so, Father: for so it seemed good in thy sight" (Matt. 11:25, 26).

"Propitiation *through faith in his*[Christ's] blood" (Rom. 3:25) is the method of reconciling a sinful people to God according to His revelation, and even the most righteous among us cannot deny that we are sinners. It was on the basis of the utilization of God's revealed plan of redemption that we are told: "By faith Abel offered unto God a more excellent sacrifice than Cain, by which he obtained witness that he was righteous, God testifying of his gifts:

and by it he being dead yet speaketh" (Heb. 11:4).

Many, like Cain, would like to offer something else than a blood sacrifice in the hope that God will be thus placated. Yet God is sovereign in His appointed plans and purposes. When He has ordained that this is the method by which He reconciles sinful men to Himself, that fact constitutes the rationale of the method, and any failure upon our part to understand why it should be thus must be laid to our own weak understanding. Much more is this true as regards any sentiment of supposed repulsiveness of a blood sacrifice.

Actually, medically speaking, there is little justification for the sentiment that blood sacrifice is repulsive to our natures. We live in an era when many lives are being saved by the timely administration of blood transfusion. In Leviticus 17:11 we are told "the life of the flesh is in the blood." Modern medical science has demonstrated this over and over again from the standpoint of: (1) nutrition; (2) support of activity through supplying tissues with the necessary oxygen and removal of waste products, and (3) combating disease through its white blood cells which at times engulf bacteria, and through so-called antibodies which are present in the liquid portion of the blood, called the blood serum.

One of the unique characteristics of blood is

this last-named serological quality. Antibodies are produced by the body in response to previous exposure to bacteria or their poisons. These antibodies, by reason of circulating in the blood stream, are available to combat threatened invasion by bacteria wherever this threat may present itself. This is largely the basis upon which immunity to certain diseases is believed to be built up by the body.

Nowadays, immunity against diphtheria is usually produced in advance of exposure to the disease by the injection of a substance similar to the poison of diphtheria called diphtheria toxoid. However, it is a fact that, in those not previously immunized, diphtheria antitoxin has been effectively utilized in the treatment of diphtheria. Diphtheria antitoxin is obtained from the liquid portion of the blood (usually the serum) of a healthy animal, ordinarily a horse, which has had diphtheria toxin (the poison of the diphtheria germ) repeatedly injected into its blood stream. Injection of this diphtheria antitoxin produced from such an animal's blood is frequently dramatic in its results in that there is often produced a rapid subsidence of fever and recovery from the disease.

This serves as an analogy illustrating the mode in which the blood of our Lord Jesus Christ, the infinite Son of God, is effectual in combating the vilest of all diseases, *sin*. He, the Lamb of God without imperfection, was exposed to all kinds of sin in its germ form, as it were, and in that He did not sin, a power became available to overcome the power of sin. "For in that he himself hath suffered being tempted, he is able to succor them that are tempted" (Heb. 2:18). Being infinite Son of God and having been "in all points tempted like as we are, yet without sin" (Heb. 4:15), His blood, which was poured forth on Calvary, has, as it were, antitoxic power to save us from all sin and from all of sin's power, when applied to the heart by faith.

Furthermore, blood taken from a creature, the life of which has ceased following the injection of bacteria or their poisons, is not trustworthy, for there is the implication, or at least suspicion, that the blood was not successful in combating the disease. But we have the assurance of the efficacy of our Saviour's blood in that He ever liveth. Indeed, in I Corinthians 15:14 we are told: "If Christ be not risen, then is our preaching vain, and your faith is also vain." He lives and our faith is not vain.

One who has as a physician seen the tragedy of death from diphtheria where diphtheria antitoxin derived from animal blood serum was not used, and then on the other hand has seen the immediate and spectacular result of the injection of the antitoxin into another patient in just as serious condition, can to some degree at least, realize the spiritual tragedy of the eternal death which is the lot of those who have never had the blood of Christ applied to the heart by faith!

Moreover, faith gives assurance and well-nigh infallible proof of the truth of God to those who follow on to know Him as Lord of their lives. In Hebrews 11:1 we are informed: "Faith is the substance of things hoped for, the evidence of things not seen." This is to say that by faith we substantiate (i.e., give substance to) the revealed truth of God. By faith we gather evidence of things not seen. Those who draw close to their Lord and Master in faith are day by day accumulating such evidence in the Lord's daily guidance, His answers to their prayers, and His enablings. Those who have thus seen mountains of difficulty removed and cast into the sea, as it were, know faith's power beyond doubt.

"O taste and see" (Ps. 34:8) is the injunction of our Lord that we put faith to the test by trying it out in connection with our daily needs. Those who thus draw nigh are not disappointed but accumulate evidence until it amounts to absolute proof in their hearts. This is the evidence faith builds its proof on, the evidence of a faith that works. Moreover, its working is unique; it is "faith which worketh by love" (Gal. 5:6). Such evidence does not come out of theological debates. It is assurance.

We feel that too many seek assurance in

other ways and thus their faith dwindles. To prove these things requires glad and complete yieldedness to God. The apostle Paul exhorts us thus to yield to God when he says: "I beseech you therefore, brethren, by the mercies of God, that ye *present your bodies* a living sacrifice, holy, acceptable unto God, which is your reasonable service. And be not conformed to this world: but be ye transformed by the renewing of your mind, that ye may prove what is that good, and acceptable, and perfect, will of God" (Rom. 12:1, 2).

However, there are some who stagger at these things and ask, "How can we believe?" Actually, faith is only impossible to those who are seeking honor and glory for themselves, for our Lord in John 5:44 made this clear when He asked: "How can ye believe, which receive honor one of another, and seek not the honor that cometh from God only?"

Faith implies a willingness to ascribe all glory to the One in whom we confide. Some Christians make the mistake of starting in true faith but later on letting pride enter in, making further faith impossible. This kind of Christian never grows spiritually. We do well to let this question of our Lord search us deeply, for this matter of seeking our own honor instead of our Master's honor is very subtle. It often creeps in without notice, and one does not realize what is wrong even though perceiving that faith is gone. When *pride,* especially spiritual pride, and *self-seeking* enter, faith leaves. Let us give all the glory to God who has enabled us for our tasks. Let us ascribe all praise to the One whose love constrains us in our work. Let us not take any credit to ourselves which rightly belongs to Him.

As a physician, the writer has often marveled at the pride and self-will of patients which hinder faith in the physician, a faith which is often essential to recovery. It is not uncommon to have a patient inform the physician that he or she is unimproved, and to find that the medicine was not taken because it did not conform to his or her preconceived notion as to size, color, taste, or consistency. Thus, unaware of the tremendous strides made in purification of drugs and extraction of the potent factor in pure concentrated form, the patient may have argued that his disease is too serious and severe to be cured by any such small tablet and left the tablets in the bottle on the shelf at home. Still he wondered why he was no better, as though his seemingly specious argument, based on ignorance and pride, could get him well in place of the physician's prescription.

Oh, to taste and see what the medicine could do! Oh, for less pride in his own limited knowledge! How much more do we hinder the working of faith in the Great Physician, when the welfare of our souls is at stake, by unwillingness to follow directions, by refusal to appropriate blessings, by pride in what we think constitutes wisdom, and by arguments based upon limited knowledge of things eternal, as though the worth of God's revelation to us could be thus easily brushed aside?

Faith's goal is triumphant faith, a faith which expresses itself in victorious living. "For whatsoever is born of God overcometh the world: and this is the victory that overcometh the world, even our faith" (I John 5:4). If we have proceeded along the lines outlined above, we will arrive at triumphant faith, the faith that makes us love people because our Lord dwells within our hearts, the faith that fills our hearts with His joy and peace, the faith that enables us to overcome evil and the *power* of sin. Thus we become *world conquerors* through triumphant faith. This is what Christ expected of us as His followers when He said: "Verily, verily, I say unto you, He that believeth on me, the works that I do shall he do also; and greater works than these shall he do; because I go unto my Father" (John 14:12). It is presumptuous on our part to stop at anything short of this goal which is God's purpose for us! Let us lay hold on this promise and praise His name! "Now thanks be unto God, who always causeth us to triumph in Christ, and maketh manifest the savour of his knowledge by us in every place" (II Cor. 2:14).

Chapter 4

ESSENTIALS OF
SPIRITUAL GROWTH

*But grow in grace, and in the knowledge of our
Lord and Saviour Jesus Christ* — II PETER 3:18

As HAS BEEN INTIMATED in the preceding
chapters, important as it is that there be a spiritual new birth so as to effect the beginning of
spiritual life, it is just as important that there
be growth in the life of the Spirit. Unfortunately, this is often overlooked. In the physical
realm there is great rejoicing over a new life
begun when the physical birth of an infant
takes place. This is because we assume that the
parents, the house in which they live, available
food supplies and sanitation, the community,
the schools, the churches, and the playgrounds
being what they are, proper growth is going to
follow. However, this may or may not be the
case. Nothing could, for instance, be more dis-
appointing than to find that development does

not take place because of an innate mental deficiency or physical deformity. Perhaps boundless love and abundant supply of food and playthings are lavished upon the offspring, and yet growth does not take place, or if it does take place, the child becomes like a brute beast as a juvenile delinquent or has otherwise grown in a way that is a disappointment to the parents and others.

If such lack of growth is possible in the physical realm, how much more should we be concerned about steady growth taking place in the spiritual realm! Yet somehow we can be very complacent over the whole matter. People who are concerned that no nutrient be lacking in the physical realm for their nutrition will willfully permit themselves to starve spiritually, apparently fearful lest they be judged as being lacking in conformity to the world about them. Yet the Bible makes it clear that conformity to the world must be cast aside while transformation into Christlikeness takes place, for in Romans 12:2 we read: "Be not conformed to this world: but be ye transformed by the renewing of your mind, that ye may prove what is that good, and acceptable, and perfect, will of God."

It is to be observed that the Bible gives as great an emphasis to Christian growth as it does to the actual message of salvation. It appears to us that spiritual starvation is in many instances the reason for lack of spiritual growth in many

Christians today. This in turn accounts, we believe, for the prevalence of diseases which stem from emotional tensions in Christian people, for we are convinced that when adequate attention is given to factors which produce spiritual growth, there is usually little or no difficulty encountered in connection with diseased states caused by emotional tensions.

In the physical realm the following factors are regarded as important in connection with promotion of proper growth: (1) proper quantity and quality of food; (2) fresh air; (3) rest and shelter; (4) exercise; (5) sanitation. The spiritual counterparts of these are deemed of equal importance with regard to spiritual growth.

The food of the Christian is the Bible, the Word of God. Job said: "I have esteemed the words of his mouth more than my necessary food" (Job 23:12). Our Lord Jesus said: "Man shall not live by bread alone, but by every word that proceedeth out of the mouth of God" (Matt. 4:4). It is only as we partake of this spiritual nourishment by taking time to meditate upon it and actually making it a part of us that we can say that we are availing ourselves of the necessary food for our own spiritual growth. It can be no excuse for the Christian to neglect this growth factor just because he is ostensibly too busy. Busy as he is, he practically always finds time to partake of material food which to Job was less to be esteemed!

Physical breathing takes place so automatically that sometimes we forget how essential it is to life. The fact is that life can exist only a matter of minutes after breathing ceases. The spiritual counterpart of breathing is prayer. As said the hymn-writer: "Prayer is the Christian's vital breath, the Christian's native air." We are enjoined to "Pray without ceasing" (I Thess. 5:17) which would seem to mean that a prayerful attitude of heart is to be ever in evidence even as we never cease to breathe. Prayer is not, however, as automatic as physical breathing. Often it requires striving like the apostle Paul together with others in our prayers (Rom. 15:30). We do well to heed the exhortation of the Epistle to the Hebrews: "Let us therefore come boldly unto the throne of grace, that we may obtain mercy, and find grace to help in time of need" (4:16).

Periods of rest and relaxation and sleep in particular, together with proper protection that is afforded from the climatic elements, are essential to physical growth. All of us can recall seeing pale, undernourished children because of inadequate sleep and the bustling environment in which they live. Spiritual growth similarly requires a shelter from the storm of life (Ps. 61:3, 4) and the rest for the people of God (Heb. 4:9). This is found in simple faith, faith that rests in the Lord and waits patiently for Him (Ps. 37:7). We enter into this rest when we cease from our own works, as God did from His (Heb. 4:10) and simply let the Holy Spirit work in us both to will and to do of His good pleasure (Phil. 2:13). It is in such surroundings that spiritual growth takes place.

Bodily exercise is important in connection with physical growth. As the infant swings his arms and legs around, the muscles of the body are exercised and growth ensues. So also spiritual growth is conditioned upon spiritual exercise in the form of active Christian witness. Often have we seen the wasting of muscles which are no longer exercised because of paralysis from poliomyelitis. This reminds us how essential it is that physical muscles be used. Wasting of the soul may well be anticipated in like fashion when spiritual exercise is not indulged in the form of active testimony to God's saving grace as we have been appointed to do by our Lord Himself when He said, "Ye shall be witnesses unto me" (Acts 1:8).

Finally, physical growth is readily retarded in an unhygienic environment. The author's experience with giving medical care to peoples in underprivileged and underdeveloped regions of the earth has demonstrated to him clearly that physical growth is in general retarded in these areas. Yet how many Christians are endeavoring to foster spiritual life in unsanitary environments from the standpoint of spiritual contamination! The emotional ills in which these folk permit themselves to live is appalling. Even more shocking is the complacency with which at times Christian people view their situation when the contaminating factors of fear, anxiety, resentfulness, and indecision are pointed out to them. We are convinced that only as spiritual sanitation is put into practice are we going to have the spiritual health and vigor that is needed to produce the full-grown spiritually mature Christian lives that God wants to see in us.

Some of the spiritual contaminants which are hindrances to Christian growth are:

1. Perfectionism attempted through the energy of the flesh, discussed in chapter 5.

2. Fear, anxiety and worry, discussed in chapter 6.

3. Bitterness, resentfulness, and lack of a forgiving spirit, discussed in chapter 7.

4. Doubt, or failure to believe and lay claim to God's promises, discussed in chapter 8.

5. Indecision and failure to discern God's will, discussed in chapter 9.

6. Lack of rest, relaxation, and recreation by failure to regiment one's time, discussed in chapter 10.

7. Jealousy and boredom through failure to rejoice in the Lord always, discussed in chapter 11.

8. Selfishness, discussed in chapter 12.

Since these spiritual contaminants are to be regarded as outstanding hindrances in the spiritual growth of the Christian in this our day, we are going to discuss in further detail the teaching of the Scriptures on these matters primarily from the standpoint of prevention of the ills stemming from them. Let us give heed to the matter of building ourselves up along scriptural lines according to the exhortation: "But ye, beloved, building up yourselves on your most holy faith, praying in the Holy Spirit, keep yourselves in the love of God, looking for the mercy of our Lord Jesus Christ unto eternal life" (Jude 20, 21, A.S.V.).

As to the treatment of the ills produced by these spiritual contaminants, that is largely outside of the scope of this book except insofar as the cure is effected by the elimination of the causative factors. Indeed, in the absence of complications recovery not infrequently occurs on this basis.

Chapter 5

AVOIDING PERFECTIONISM

Are ye so foolish? Having begun in the Spirit, are ye now made perfect by the flesh? —
GALATIANS 3:3

PERFECTIONISM is a term frequently used by modern psychologists to refer to an attitude on the part of an individual that represents dissatisfaction with any achievement that is short of perfection, regardless of how fitted or ill-fitted he is to attain to it. From the standpoint of the Bible, we use the term similarly except that we believe that in the place of perfection there is a completeness, which is ours, not attained through fleshly striving and effort, but obtained through the power of the Holy Spirit who makes us complete in God (Col. 2:10).

Actually the perfectionism, of which the modern psychologist speaks, differs in no respect from the perfectionism attempted by the Galatian church which the apostle Paul so vehement-

ly condemned when he asked: "Are ye so foolish? Having begun in the Spirit, are ye now
made perfect by the flesh?" (Gal. 3:3).

The reason for the existence of the life of the
Spirit is our inability to be righteous without it.
Yet somehow we foolishly look back and start
in to attempt to do what we at first knew we
could never do, as though all we needed was a
fresh start and then we could make out all right.
This is not true, for "by the deeds of the law
there shall no flesh be justified in his sight"
(Rom. 3:20). Right through to the finish we
need the power of the Spirit to work unhindered in full sway in our lives so as to bring to
completion the good work which was started
in us at the time of the new birth when we be-
gan in the Spirit.

The perfectionist often is guilty of attempting
that which he is utterly incapable of accomplishing. This may or may not be obvious to
him. Often he is aware of it in his subconscious
mind to the extent that he provides for the inevitable state of frustration which is going to
face him through prearranged excuses and
blame which is set on other people. Some perfectionists actually seem to gloat in their frustrations and apparently endeavor to make sure
that they are once more going to land themselves into a frustrated state by refusing the
help of those who stand in readiness to assist
them. Moreover, instead of tackling a job for

which he is suited, the perfectionist will often insist on attempting that in which he is neither trained nor experienced. As he views failure looming up, he quickly points out that if only he had this or that gadget (sometimes the latest new-fangled type of desk, for instance), he could successfully accomplish his task. The gadget is obtained. The task is again attempted and failure ensues. This time the emotional tension fuse burns out and an emotional tension pattern, usually of the stiff-neck type, becomes evident.

This is the type of symptom pattern which we physicians see so frequently in our offices. Each time a new frustration comes along, perhaps every few months, the sufferer is back in our office. At times the patient vaguely realizes that tensions have built up. Sometimes the patient believes that he must be contracting some new disease, possibly he thinks this time it is cancer.

The alert physician, however, as he sees his patient again, recognizes the old tension pattern, possibly with slight variation this time. He inquires into recent episodes of attempting the impossible with consequent frustration and usually the inquiry brings out another episode of attempted perfectionism.

Well do I remember the last such episode I saw in one of these perfectionists. She was a Christian woman and had been coming to the office with a renewed episode of the stiff-neck tension pattern resulting from a fresh frustration about every six or eight months. This time she had resolved to get her husband, who was in his late thirties, into college. Her husband was successful in his line of work and there was little reason that appealed to us for his changing his status. It seemed clear to us that there was a striving for an all-inclusive perfectionism that could not be justified. The college wisely considered this an ill-advised move, presumably on the basis of his previous mediocre scholarship and unsettled type of career, and refused him admission. The wife, however, insisted that the college admissions office was to be blamed for not discerning the needs of her husband. Thus she landed herself in severe frustration and the stiff-neck tension pattern reproduced itself.

All we could do in this instance was to convince her that she was suffering from emotional tension and give her treatment for it. Her unbending attitude made her entirely blind to the source from which her tension had arisen. Indeed, she had so conditioned herself to living in the climate of frustration that it did not appeal to her to release the college from blame and perhaps blame herself with a view to avoiding such an episode again.[1]

---

[1] To her credit, however, let it be said that some months later she returned and spontaneously told us how she had found release from her emotional tensions when she came to the realization that she was "rebellious."

It is true that the Scripture says, "As for God, his way is perfect" (Ps. 18:30). This, however, is a perfection which comes from above and is not attained through our own effort, as we have clearly shown from the Scripture references quoted in the first part of this chapter. It is for us to lay claim to the perfection and completeness which is provided through our Lord and Saviour. This is not sinless perfection. It is not perfectionism. It is a righteousness which is imputed to us through Christ by faith, as Paul tells us in Romans 4:24: "For us also, to whom it shall be imputed, if we believe on him." It is a completeness which is only accomplished when we are dwelling in Him, having ceased from our own imperfect efforts to attain that completeness.

Frustration comes to the perfectionist because he has first of all frustrated the grace of God in a manner in which Paul refused so to do when he said: "I do not frustrate the grace of God: for if righteousness come by the law, then Christ is dead in vain" (Gal. 2:21). In other words *frustration can only come to the Christian who is frustrating the grace of God*. Frustrating the grace of God is not what God intends for His child.

The fact is that God has told us that He is able to make all grace abound toward us; that we always having all sufficiency in all things, may abound to every good work (II Cor. 9:8).

How dare we as Christians thus surrounded with the abundance of God's grace push it away from us by frustrating the grace of God! It actually takes more effort on our part for us to push away the grace of God from us than to let His grace abound in our lives. This leaves us with no excuse for turning toward perfectionism. We should nip such attitudes in the bud before we allow ourselves to get into the stubborn state of the stiff-neck emotional tension pattern.

It is no wonder then that the apostle Paul emphasized and re-emphasized to the early Christians the primacy of God's grace, invoking God's grace upon them at the beginning of his letters, at the end and throughout his letters to them, in such words as those we read in I Thessalonians 5:28: "The grace of our Lord Jesus Christ be with you. Amen."

We are aware that often there is a seemingly appropriate incentive for seeking fleshly perfectionism. Few of us want to be obvious hypocrites, least of all those of us who profess to be Christians. In fact, we often find that the Christian is ready to patch up his appearance, which he guards carefully under the guise of his Christian testimony before men, lest he bring reproach upon the name of Christ. Unfortunately in doing so, sometimes he is accomplishing just the opposite of that which he set out to do. The performance in the energy of the flesh may become even more obvious to the non-Christian observer than to himself that it is a sham.

We believe that the indwelling Spirit of God will accomplish God's will in the believer without any fleshly endeavor and least of all without any pretense on his part. This is frequently without any consciousness on his part that anything is transpiring. Such was the case with Moses, for we learn that he "wist not that the skin of his face shone" while at the same time the shining of his face was clearly seen by the children of Israel (Exod. 34:29, 30, 35).

Lives that shine can and should be the effect of our living in the power of the Spirit of God. Fleshly perfectionism is a poor substitute for this. Having begun in the Spirit, we have the assurance that God's work in us can be best brought to fruition by letting His Spirit continue His work within us, for Paul reminds us in I Thessalonians 5:24: "Faithful is he that calleth you, who also will do it."

That which is accomplished in us by the indwelling Spirit of God is characterized by innate spontaneity and completeness. In contrast, that which is done in the energy of the flesh is characterized by a forced man-made artificiality and rarely if ever attains to its goal of perfection.

Chapter 6

FEAR NOT

Fear thou not; for I am with thee: be not dismayed; for I am thy God: I will strengthen thee; yea, I will help thee; yea, I will uphold thee with the right hand of my righteousness.
—Isaiah 41:10

In the relative simplicity of life in Old Testament times, it appears that there was a greater awareness of the important part which fear plays in deterring us from buoyant healthy living. Indeed, David who met and vanquished the giant Goliath speaks of his deliverance from fear as from one of the strongest enemies that had come against him when he said: "I sought the Lord, and he heard me, and delivered me from all my fears" (Ps. 34:4).

It would appear that all too frequently we compromise with this archenemy and in our promised land we let him settle down peaceably alongside us instead of driving him out.

Yet the Lord tells us definitely in His Word that fear is to have no place in us, and we are *commanded*, "Fear not."

Many a life is controlled, or is out of control, as the case may be, by reason of fear. We are fearful that friends will fail us. We are fearful that sickness will come, bringing hardship. We are fearful that we cannot hold out. We are fearful that our national mistakes will catch up with us. We are fearful that our personal mistakes will be our ruin. On every side we are surrounded by fears.

But perhaps you say nobody knows your fears. Maybe you are successfully hiding them behind a joking, grinning facial mask for the time being, but that pile of fears cannot forever accumulate within you without a profound effect. The very thing you feared — sickness — comes, not because your body is worn out, but simply because that collection of fears has reached the point where it can no longer be contained.

Constant fear is not normal for the human being. It utilizes the special alarm system of the human body which is fundamentally a mechanism for taking care of emergencies. No matter how good it is, like a fire-alarm system, it eventually breaks down when called upon every day and every hour of the day to function in what should, in most instances, not be of an emergency nature.

How then can we deal with our fears? Often the answer comes, "Through resolution not to fear." However, that is like trying to cut the electric wires of your fire-alarm system. Your city is not better off by cutting the wires on your fire-alarm system just because there have been too many false alarms! No, this is not the answer. The fears are still there despite your resolve. The fears must be banished.

The real remedy is replacing our fear of man and circumstances with *the fear of God,* which is reverential trust in Him with hatred of evil. When true trust in God enters, fear of man departs. Trust in God and fear of man cannot abide together.

David, the psalmist, learned the conquest of fear as he roamed the land of Palestine pursued by an insane ruler whose mental aberrations he had formerly appeased with his harp. Not even music could slow up the alarm system in either Saul or David any more. The fears had to be dealt with, and having learned the secret, David burst forth in song: "What time I am afraid, I will trust in thee" (Ps. 56:3).

Only God can deliver from fear of man and circumstances. He provides complete salvation through faith in Jesus Christ, the Saviour, who shed His blood upon the cross of Calvary to deliver us from all sin, including the sin of fear, for the Bible tells us clearly that "the fearful . . . shall have their part in the lake which burneth with fire and brimstone: which is the second death" (Rev. 21:8).

It was doubtless with a foreview of this that the prophet Isaiah went one step farther than David when he exclaimed: "Behold, God is my salvation; I *will trust, and not be afraid*" (Isa. 12:2), apparently meaning that trust in God acted as a preventive to prevent fear of man and circumstances from ever even confronting him.

Nevertheless it is noteworthy that the Lord's people have been prone to compromise with fear and let it live unmolested in their midst. It is no wonder then that our Lord Jesus' coming into the world was heralded and accompanied throughout with a new declaration of war on fear and with renewed orders to the Lord's people to put fear away. Impressive is the array of these peremptory commands from God Himself: (1) "Fear not, Zacharias" (Luke 1:13); (2) "Fear not, Mary" (Luke 1:30); (3) "Joseph, thou son of David, fear not" (Matt. 1:20); (4) shepherds, "fear not" (Luke 2:10); (5) "Simon, fear not" (Luke 5:10); (6) "Fear not, little flock" (Luke 12:32); and (7) at the tomb, "Women, fear not ye" (Matt. 28:5). Similarly Jesus asked His disciples in Mark 4:40: "Why are ye so fearful? How is it that ye have no faith?" In so doing, He again made it clear that fear of man and circumstances presents a mutually exclusive alternative with faith in God. Obviously with this in view it is incon-

ceivable that faith and fear may dominate in
the same heart.

Anxiety and worry represent forms of fear
which project themselves into the future and
often concern themselves with imaginary situations which never come to pass. Indeed, it often
happens when the future situation arrives, it is
devoid of all the contemplated elements which
were anticipated, much as David observed in
Psalm 53:5 when he said: "There were they in
great fear, where no fear was." Nevertheless,
the fear element in anxiety and worry is just as
real as any fear, even though the thing feared
proves to be entirely a figment of the imagination. From this standpoint it is to be seen that
anxiety and worry produce just as severe emotional tension disease patterns as fear itself.

Well has it been said: "Anxiety never baked
a cake, built a bridge, won a battle, or solved a
problem. Important as we are, we really render
ourselves less useful, and less important, if we
let worry stall our actions."

As our Lord Jesus observed anxiety and worry
in His disciples, He said in Matthew 6:28-30:
"Consider the lilies of the field, how they grow;
they toil not, neither do they spin: and yet I
say unto you, That even Solomon in all his glory
was not arrayed like one of these. Wherefore, if
God so clothe the grass of the field, which today is, and tomorrow is cast into the oven, shall

he not much more clothe you, O ye of little
faith?"

Thus our Lord Jesus contrasts the fear of
anxiety and worry with faith in God just as did
David and Isaiah. It would appear, indeed, that
we are confronted with a mathematical expression to the effect that fear of man is inversely
proportional to faith in God.

Passing on into the Epistle to the Philippians,
the apostle Paul, writing under the inspiration
of the Spirit (4:6, A.S.V.), says: "In nothing be
anxious; but in everything by prayer and supplication with thanksgiving let your requests be
made known unto God." The gist of this passage
seems to be that if the Christian finds himself
prone to advance into the future through the
use of his imagination to guess at what may be
going to happen, this is a call to prayer in which
the future is wholly committed to God who cannot do wrong.

Finally, when fear is thus dealt with, "the
peace of God, which passeth all understanding"
(i.e., is not explainable purely on the ground
of logic) "shall guard your hearts and your
thoughts in Christ Jesus" (Phil. 4:7, A.S.V.). In
other words, faith in God comes to dispel fear,
and when fear has gone, an inexplicable peace
prevails in the heart. This is in accord with the
words of our Lord Jesus: "Peace I leave with
you, my peace I give unto you: not as the world

giveth, give I unto you. Let not your heart be troubled, neither let it be afraid" (John 14:27).

However, it is to be noted that fear, anxiety, and worry come upon us most subtly. It is for us to be on our guard lest they find any lodgment in the heart.

Our experience with an earnest evangelical pastor comes to mind in this connection. About fifty years old and in a pastorate in a large city, he was successful in his ministry, for through it many young people were finding salvation in Christ, and many were being induced to dedicate their lives to the Lord for full-time Christian service. Nevertheless, he was feeling increasing and unrelenting pressure from his church board to keep up and improve these good results in his work, even though past the prime of life and less able physically to make as many visitations to homes in the community as formerly. Emotional tensions were being built up within him as the result of this anxiety and a certain degree of resentment toward his church board.

These tensions expressed themselves principally in the chest tension pattern and he came to us for medical help, convinced, as it were, that he had genuine heart trouble. We gave him a thorough physical examination including chest X-ray and electrocardiogram, but found no evidence of organic heart disease. Besides, his symptom pattern was typical of the chest tension pattern.

At first he seemed to be unaware of the presence of any worry or anxiety. However, as we pressed the matter home to him, it suddenly dawned on him that he was worried and he said, "You have no idea of the pressure under which we pastors are working in this city. If I do not show an annual increase in my statistics, I am liable to have to leave my position as a pastor. I am getting too old to take up any other kind of work, such as the grocery business. I just have to satisfy the church board or I have no way of supporting my family."

Quietly we looked at him for a moment, aware that he was a choice vessel of the Lord, remarkably owned and used of Him, but that he had fallen into this pitfall of worry and probably an element of resentfulness along with it that might have happened to any of the rest of us, if we had been off our guard. Finally, we asked him the question which he was doubtless starting to ask himself as he had brought things out into the open before his own eyes for the first time, "Whom are you serving: the church board or the Lord Jesus Christ?"

The answer was ready almost before we got the question out. Indeed, how could he have ever acted as though he was serving the church board? He had long ago resolved to serve the Lord Jesus Christ only and this was still his sole ambition. I could see that the anxiety was gone as a new peace crept over his face.

One week later the pastor brought one of his young people, a young lady, to our office for physical examination as a candidate for the mission field. After completion of the physical examination, I discussed her suitability for missionary work with him privately and then said, "By the way, what has happened to those heart pains?"

With a smile on his face, he appreciatingly said, "Oh, the Lord has taken care of all that. Praise His name, I have no more pain."

It truly rejoiced our heart to see the prompt recovery from disease symptoms which took place when this emotional factor of worry was dealt with in a forthright manner before the face of our Lord Jesus.

It is our firm conviction that the Christian has the full armamentarium to deal with fear, anxiety, and worry through faith in our Lord and Saviour Jesus Christ. When fear is not dealt with forthrightly as the above pastor did, it represents compromise on our part just as the Israelites compromised with the inhabitants of Canaan whom God had commanded them to drive out from the land in the days of Joshua. God told them that he had delivered these Canaanite nations into their hands but the Israelites simply neglected to drive them out and thus appropriate their victory. These nations became, as God had foretold, thorns in their side to vex them (Num. 33:55).

As soldiers of the cross, we have received our orders, "Fear not!" We must respond with as prompt obedience as if we were soldiers on the march while serving in a human army who had received the command, "Halt!" Just two steps are allowed for the march to cease. The personal command of our Captain, the Lord Christ, "Fear not!" can and should receive as implicit and prompt obedience primarily because He is our Lord and Master, but also because of the dire consequences which disobedience works in our own lives.

Remember that if there is any retained spirit of fear after we have heard this command, we are holding on to something that is not of Him: "For God hath not given us the spirit of fear; but of power, and of love, and of a sound mind" (II Tim. 1:7).

Chapter 7

AS WE FORGIVE

Then said Jesus, Father, forgive them; for they know not what they do. — Luke 23:34

Misgivings as to the import of the phrase, "Forgive us our trespasses as we forgive them who trespass against us," are sometimes encountered. We are told by some that this is a prayer which we as Christians cannot pray since forgiveness is offered freely to us through faith in Christ and in this age of grace is not conditioned upon our forgiving others. Moreover, it is said that our Lord Jesus was giving the so-called "Lord's Prayer" to His disciples as their prayer while they were still living under the dispensation of the law, and that things have so completely changed as the result of the forgiveness made possible by His subsequent death on the cross for us that we should no longer consider forgiveness as based upon anything we can do. Indeed, we are enjoined not even to ask for forgiveness since forgiveness through Christ's death on the cross is an already accomplished fact which we are encouraged to appropriate to ourselves. From this standpoint, we cannot properly forgive others until we have experienced God's forgiveness. Then our forgiving others becomes a natural outflow of having been forgiven.

That this attitude has a great measure of truth to support it, we cannot deny. However, it does not take into account the fact that regardless of whether we are living under the dispensation of law or under the dispensation of grace, the enjoyment of God's forgiveness always bears a reciprocal relationship to our experience of forgiving one another. It appeals to us that this relationship is based upon an ebb and flow which gradually tends to reach a point of equilibrium. From this standpoint the experience of forgiving one another enhances our enjoyment and appropriation of the fruit of God's forgiveness, and vice versa, our experience of God's forgiveness enhances our capacity to forgive one another.

It appears that the word *as*, small as it is, is the delimiting word and keynote of the expression, "Forgive as we forgive." From the dictionary we get its meaning: "To the extent or degree of or in which; in the manner in which; like." Now we can eliminate the latter meanings as definitely inappropriate here. No matter in what age or dispensation we live, we do not liken God's forgiveness in its infiniteness to human forgiveness, nor are we asking God to limit Himself in His forgiveness to the manner in which we human beings forgive one another. It therefore follows that the word *as* refers to the extent or degree in which God's forgiveness becomes applied to us. God's forgiveness remains infinite, but its experience and application to ourselves unfortunately is limited and that by our own selves.

It is our conviction that we on the human side are limiting the experience and application of forgiveness in unnecessary ways. It is with the hope of clarifying this that we wish to elucidate further the meaning of the expression, "Forgive us as we forgive."

When God says He forgives, He says: "Their sins and their iniquities will I *remember no more*" (Heb. 8:12). Although many of us confess to having poor memories, probably none of us can be as forgetful of sin as God. The person who says he can forgive but never forget is trying to do the impossible. Forgiveness involves forgetting past sins. When these sins are again called up, it means that the so-called forgiveness was spurious. When we bring to mind in any kind of an anxious mood the sins which we have in the past already confessed to God, it is because we doubt God's Word that He is faithful and just to forgive us our sins (I John 1:9), since God has told us that He has forgotten all about it. Similarly, when we again bring up the sins of our fellow men whom we professedly had forgiven, we show that we had never really forgiven them since forgiveness involves remembering the involved sins no more. Furthermore, if we have not forgotten our neighbor's sin in our professed forgiveness of him, we show that we have not comprehended the meaning of the word *forgive* and therefore can scarcely have entered into the enjoyment of God's forgiveness of us.

Our Lord Jesus illustrated this clearly in His parable of the debtor in Matthew 18:23-35 where we see the man, whose ten-thousand-talent debt was mercifully canceled in response to his request, sending to prison the man who owed him only one hundred pence. The repercussions were tremendous when the creditor of the ten-thousand-talent debt heard of these dealings. The degree of insincerity shown made it obvious that he was acting unworthily of the forgiveness proffered, and that he had utterly failed to comprehend the spirit of forgiveness shown him. Our Lord Jesus concluded with the eternal principle applicable to man in all dispensations: "So likewise shall my heavenly Father do also unto you, if ye from your hearts forgive not every one his brother their trespasses" (Matt. 18:35).

To clarify more fully the meaning of the

words, "Forgive as we forgive," a bit of para-phrasing seems in order. When we consider the import of the Lord's prayer in asking God to do all for us out of recognition of our own help-lessness, even to the extent of delivering us from evil, we may give voice to this helplessness in both receiving and giving forgiveness by say-ing, "Forgive us and keep us ever forgiving others," for we may well doubt whether it is to be implied that we have the power to forgive others in our own strength when we acknowl-edge to God, "Thine is the power" (Matt. 6:13). Again, it would appear that the implication of our request is, "Fill us with Thy grace in for-giving us while all the time we are being emptied of our resentments so that we can con-tain it all." More simply we may pray, "Grant us forgiveness in hearts prepared by forgiving."

The Word of God makes it clear that it is bitterness and resentment that bar the way to forgiveness, for it is clearly pointed out that the grace of God is the antithesis of bitterness in Hebrews 12:15 where we are admonished to be "looking diligently lest any man fail of the grace of God." This failure on one's part to appro-priate the grace of God is further attributed in this Scripture to "any root of bitterness spring-ing up" so as to trouble us and defile many. It is clear that the spirit of bitterness and resent-ment and the fullness of God's grace cannot co-exist in the same human heart. Bitterness drives out grace and, besides, defiles many. It is for us to make our choice as to which we will have. The apostle Peter clearly tells us what our choice should be when he says: "Not rendering evil for evil, or railing for railing: but *contrariwise blessing;* knowing that ye are thereunto called, that ye should inherit a blessing" (I Peter 3:9). It is the *contrariwise blessing* of forgiving others that opens to us the inheritance of the blessing of God's grace and forgiveness.

For us to come to God with an unforgiving spirit toward our fellow creatures, while ostensibly reaching out for His forgiveness, is hypocrisy. Infinite though God's forgiveness is, it should be obvious that we cannot enter into possession of it under these circumstances. It is like holding a tightly stoppered bottle under Niagara Falls while we wonder why never a drop of water enters it. Despite the overabundance of water, the stopper must be removed in order that the bottle may be filled with water. Just so must the plug of selfish resentment be removed from us before we can enjoy the fullness of God's grace in forgiveness. May God help us to forget our resentments as He can forget! No more should we apologize for our poor memories when we forget some triviality. It merely reflects on the fact that we are concentrating our powers of memory on the areas of resentments and bitterness in which God concentrates His forgetfulness. Doubtless our memories could be improved for remembering the right sort of things if we were not overtaxing them and cluttering them with bitter dregs in this way. If we could only forget like God, our thirsty minds would avidly pick up the thoughts which are true, honest, just, pure, lovely, and of good report, together with virtue and praise such as should characterize our thinking (Phil. 4:8).

Supremely, we see this in our Lord Jesus as He hung on the cross. The world could well understand how the treatment it had accorded Him could cause Him to harbor bitterness and resentment toward those, both Jews and Romans, who had thus seemingly blighted His ministry and put Him into a position of extreme shame and painful suffering. Yet then and there amid it all, He was able to forgive and forget it all as He cried: "Father, forgive them, for they know not what they do." His forgiveness was proffered even in the absence of any asking for forgiveness on the part of those forgiven, so gracious and complete was it.

The bitterness and resentment of the unforgiving spirit, progressing sometimes even into anger, makes for emotional tension build-up most commonly of the stomach tension symptom pattern as mentioned in chapter 1. When unrelieved, the condition may proceed into definite peptic ulcer formation. Well has it been said of the stomach tension symptom pattern, and in particular of peptic ulcer, that it is not so much a matter of what the patient eats, as it is a matter of what is eating him.

Illustrative of this is the case of a patient whom we will call Mrs. Oliver who was under our observation for some three years, chiefly for the stomach tension symptom pattern, although at times there was evidence of the other two principal tension symptom patterns mentioned in chapter 1. She was the only member of her family who was a Christian, but she was an earnest Christian. This made her the more sensitive to the persecution which she received at the hands of her husband and other members of the family. More recently her husband has come under our medical care for duodenal peptic ulcer and this tends to point to mutual resentment on the part of both husband and wife. Gradually Mrs. Oliver had allowed herself to get obviously provoked and resentful over seeming trifles. For instance, Mr. Oliver would put unseemly music on the phonograph on Sunday so that he could apparently take pleasure in seeing how it affected his wife. A vicious circle had thereby been established and was continuing, and this was causing increasing resentfulness on the wife's part and increased the "fedup" emotional tension symptoms of her stomach.

Finally, Mrs. Oliver came to the place where she saw things in their true light. She was reminded of how our Lord acted. "Who, when he was reviled, reviled not again; when he suffered, he threatened not; but *committed* himself to him that judgeth righteously" (I Peter 2:23). Then and there she committed all these things to her Saviour and Lord. Her husband was forgiven because she was willing to assume that he knew no better, and she applied Christ's words on the cross to the situation in saying: "Forgive him, for he knows not what he does."

She soon came back to our office testifying that her husband was sweeter than ever to her. Moreover, she realized that this was largely because she had become sweeter through the Lord's grace. Mrs. Oliver's resentfulness had gone, and with it, all her physical ailments. Her husband had for the first time accompanied her to church. Her joy in the Lord had become full and running over. She no longer needs stomach medicines, but she came to our office to thank us for what had been done for her in pointing the way.

As for Mr. Oliver, he has shown some improvement but is still under medical care. While the actual existence of the peptic ulcer necessarily complicates the picture, yet there is good reason to anticipate even more definite improvement if and when he opens his heart to the Saviour and finds forgiveness and peace his portion through His grace.

Again I think of a college student, whom we will speak of as Jack. Jack was an ardent Christian young man, the son of missionary parents. In his childhood his life had been remarkably spared by what indubitably seemed to all concerned to be divine intervention. Before coming to America to go to college, Jack wrote ahead giving the college information as to his previous academic courses. The college had notified him that he was being admitted to the freshman class and also certified to the United States Government that this was the case so that he could as a British subject gain admittance to the United States.

However, when Jack reached the college, he found that another semester of high school work was being required before admission to college. He became resentful over this but did take the high school work and later entered the college. His resentment continued. As he needed to work his way through and at the same time wanted to make up the seemingly lost time of the semester which he spent in high school, he overburdened himself with college studies beyond his physical capacity. As we analyze his actions, it would appear that there was an attitude of spite engrafted on his resentfulness and bitterness. At the close of his final examinations one June, he came to us, a victim of an acute peptic ulcer.

Medical treatment had to be given, and his schedule of work in the factory as well as of his studies had to be lightened. After some months of treatment, however, it became obvious that there were factors retarding his recovery. It was then that Jack's harbored resentment was exposed to us as we cross-questioned him. It is anticipated that as he deals with this resentment on a spiritual plane, more definite improvement will take place, as is so often the case.

In this connection it is to be pointed out that it should never be a concern to the individual involved as to whether the person or party who is apparently guilty of the wrong shows a true attitude of repentance. The principal wrong which is being done is that which one does to himself in harboring bitterness, and this causes far greater injury in most cases than can be inflicted upon him by another person. We must pray: "Father, forgive them for they know not what they do," and not take the attitude that we must extract from the one whom we think has wronged us a confession of his guilt before we forgive. Indeed, it is just as well for us to admit that ignorance on someone's part may well have been the source of the apparent wrongdoing.

Another patient we might refer to under the name of Mrs. Jones. She too had all three of the emotion tension symptom patterns mentioned in chapter 1, but suffered chiefly with the stomach tension pattern which she referred to as nervous indigestion. Drug therapy gave her a measure of relief, only to give greater prominence to her stiff-neck symptom pattern. Reared in a Christian family, she had nevertheless come to the place where she harbored deep-seated bitterness and resentment which she could stomach no longer, as it were. Her mother-in-law and father-in-law were not on speaking terms with her and had even refused to see her little girl. A minor degree of resentment was felt toward her husband for letting things get into this state. Gradually this story had unraveled itself. As she faced some of the minor factors in connection with her resentments and sought to forgive, symptoms started to clear. However, just then her mother-in-law became seriously ill. Her husband suggested that flowers be sent. She demurred as she recalled that her husband had not permitted her to send flowers when her own mother was sick. Resentment once more flourished and with it the stiff neck with its severe neuritis and headache. Finally, we confronted her with the fact that the real remedy was to send flowers to her mother-in-law. She refused, and her physical condition definitely worsened in consequence. We are convinced that a forgiving attitude is the only real remedy for such a case, for only thus are the causal resentments permanently cleared away.

We might also mention others, particularly the woman who became resentful toward God Himself for taking her husband in a heart attack, with consequent bitterness toward everyone and toward life in general. A stiff, painful neck and pains in the region of the heart gave physical expression to the overflowing, though suppressed, resentments within. Moreover, it scarcely seemed to be mere coincidence that her resentments also expressed themselves in the hat that she wore, bristling as it did with what looked like porcupine quills.

As Christians, no matter who we may be, it is incumbent upon us to face realities and not allow ourselves to drift into being merely lukewarm Christians who are endeavoring to avoid going more than halfway in God's way — to our own great deprivation and loss. Forgiveness, as the central element in the Gospel, is basic and must be kept there. God's method of dealing with these matters of the Spirit is not that of temporizing or indecision, and much less of covering up sin. There must be an attitude of finality in the transactions that take place. Merely suppressing resentments and bitterness, while hoping for a better day that never comes, is not God's method of dealing with these matters. It is for us, as His children, to realize this more fully and to help those with whom we deal to come to the position before Him where these matters are dealt with in His way with the thoroughness and finality which He demands, namely, by a forgetting forgiveness.

To insist upon our rights is to insist upon

something we do not deserve, for we are all of us undeserving sinners who do not merit the grace of God bestowed upon us in saving us and making us His children through the new birth. Taking vengeance, or even planning it, also has no place in the Christian, for God says: "Vengeance is mine; I will repay, saith the Lord" (Rom. 12:19). When we take vengeance into our hands, we are dealing with stolen property. Vengeance belongs to the Lord Himself!

Only as we have a forgiving spirit do we meet the criteria needed to be recipients of God's grace in full measure and thus cast aside the yoke which we needlessly put upon ourselves when we are bitter and resentful.

Chapter 8

DOUBT NOT

Have faith, and doubt not . . . And all things, whatsoever ye shall ask in prayer, believing, ye shall receive. — MATTHEW 21:21, 22

THOUSANDS OF PROMISES for our good are given to us in the Bible. These are mostly conditioned upon our claiming them in simple faith in God. Yet so frequently we fail to put our trust in God so as to lay claim to them. The Bible calls this doubt. Sometimes we think of it as indifference. Yet the fact is, that if we really believe in God, we will neither doubt nor be indifferent to His promises.

These promises are largely to be laid hold of by faith through prayer. In this connection come to mind the words of the old hymn:

> What a Friend we have in Jesus,
> All our sins and griefs to bear!
> What a privilege to carry
> Everything to God in prayer!

O what peace we often forfeit,
O what needless pain we bear,
All because we do not carry
Everything to God in prayer!

In *doubt* we encounter another cause of emotional tensions in so-called Christian people. Having entered upon a new life based upon the grace of God in Christ Jesus, in other words, having begun by faith in God, we lose sight of the fact that the continuance of spiritual life is by the same means, that is, faith in God. We forget that just as our initial problem was solved by faith in God, so are also the subsequent problems to be solved by faith in God and that the approach to their solution is through believing prayer.

Instead, perchance, the unsolved problems are laid aside to be faced at some future time and in some other way. Unwittingly this produces emotional tensions. This is not God's way of dealing with things. This is not to say that God's time is always right away, but it does mean that we as God's children may so commit things into His hands and leave them there that there is no tantalizing tension left as we face the issue. Actually, however, our experience has been more often than not that God has been waiting for us to meet the conditions of His promises so that He might answer our prayer promptly and pour forth of His abundant blessing upon us.

Misunderstandings, hardships, trials, and testings gather round about us to challenge us. The Bible makes it clear that these are to be expected as we journey on in the Christian life. Their purpose is to challenge us into deeper faith so that we will grow more Christlike. The solution of these problems is not in evasion, as doubt and indifference would often have us do, but in claiming God's promises by faith.

Before specifically mentioning one of these promises, it should be pointed out that there is a Greek word which occurs in the New Testament which is often translated *temptation* but which has a much broader meaning than that, in that it includes also *trial* and *testing*. In fact, the word *temptation* of the Authorized Version is so translated in the margin of the ASV for James 1:2. The liberty of substituting these words and their cognates will be taken in the scriptural quotations in the paragraphs that follow.

One of the promises of God's Word which should be the frequent resource of the Christian but which is often unclaimed by him is the promise which is found in I Corinthians 10:13 in which we make the above suggested substitution of words: "There hath no trial taken you but such as is common to man: but God is faithful, who will not suffer you to be tried above that ye are able; but will with the trial also make a way to escape, that ye may be able to bear it."

So often our doubts are foolishly based upon the idea that our situation is one that neither God nor man has encountered before, and therefore we think that our problem is without solution. This overlooks the facts of the case, for in Hebrews 4:15 we are told that Christ "was in all points tried like as we are," and further in Hebrews 2:18 we read: "For in that he himself hath suffered being tried, he is able to succor them that are tried."

It has been our experience more than once that when we have faced these seemingly impossible situations squarely in simple faith, a glorious solution promptly awaits us that we never dreamed of as being possible. This is in accordance with Luke 18:27: "The things which are impossible with men are possible with God." Moreover, our hearts re-echo the words of the prophet Jeremiah: "Ah Lord God: behold, thou hast made the heaven and the earth by thy great power and stretched-out arm, and there is nothing too hard for thee" (Jer. 32:17).

In this connection there comes to mind the experience of one of our patients whom we will refer to as Mrs. Larchwood. She had been coming to us for some time because of emotional tensions. Medicines had given her a measure of relief, but it was obvious that we had not gotten very far into removing the basic cause. In the meantime I had gradually gotten to know her background, and the day approached when I was able to get her to face her situation in a straightforward manner.

I said to her, "Now, you are, I know, an earnest Christian. Can't we make an approach to solving your emotional difficulties through the power of the Lord?"

"Yes," she admitted, "I am a Christian, but I do not believe as you do. In our church we do not believe in the eternal security of the believer."

Not to be sidetracked over a side issue I simply said, "That need make no difference. The fact is that you do believe in the power of God as I do, don't you?"

"Yes, I do," she replied, "but you simply have no idea what it is to live with a drunken husband. I am sure no one ever faced my kind of problem. I simply never know what is coming next. I never know when I am going to get embarrassed to death again by his getting into a scrape with one of the neighbors, or whether I am going to be able to get him out of the scrape as I have barely done several times in the past. What can I do?"

I was resolved to get her to face the issue on a spiritual plane. I might well have told of my experiences with drunken army officers during World War II, including getting them on their knees with me in prayer. I knew, moreover, that the Bible said that her problem was such as is common to man. I therefore said to her, "That may seem to be the case. Of one thing, however, I am certain and that is that God has a ready solution for your problem in prayer. I have a promise here in the Bible that I want to read you."

Thereupon I read I Corinthians 10:13 as quoted above, substituting the words *trial* and *tried* for the words *temptation* and *tempted* as they occur in the Authorized Version. Then I asked, "Will you make a simple promise to me to claim this promise of Scripture once every day on your knees in prayer — and really mean it?"

She replied that she would, and I knew she really meant business. I also knew God had a solution to her problem, impossible though it seemed.

Actually, in my wildest imagination I never dreamed the answer would come the way it came, but, when it came, there was no doubt in either of our minds that God had heard and answered her prayer. It was about two days later that one of the doctors with whom I am affiliated received in my absence a rush call to the Larchwood home. Mr. Larchwood had had a heart attack. He realized that his life was in jeopardy. Anything the doctor would tell him to do would be carried out.

Mr. Larchwood was informed that the only way to make a safe recovery was to give up his drinking of alcoholic beverages entirely. This was advised on the basis of medical indications and not on the basis of any knowledge of the home situation or of what I had advised. The outcome was that Mr. Larchwood gave up his liquor and has not touched it again for these more than two years.

As for Mrs. Larchwood, she saw clearly the hand of God in thus answering her prayers. Her emotional tensions were relieved in great measure, and she found a new sense of security in taking things to God in prayer even though she might not have been ready to call it the eternal security of the believer.

Often to obtain the release of emotional tensions, doubt must be replaced by faith in God that simply takes God at His Word and claims His promises. Thus our problems are solved and the emotional tensions, which pile up because of them, are dispelled.

One more associated topic remains to be added. Often in the New Testament we find reference made to fasting in connection with believing prayer. Notably is this the case in connection with the beginning of the missionary movement as recorded in Acts 13:2, 3, where Paul and Barnabas were sent forth after prayer and fasting. Some of the greatest men of God in the past, such as Hudson Taylor, George

Mueller, and the Wesleys, have been men who engaged in a day or more of fasting at periodic intervals. This was done apparently in dead earnestness which looked upon the task of prayer as one that superseded food in importance at such times.

Today one sees an emphasis in the opposite direction. To start with, our American diet has been stepped up in high caloric foods, notably fats which contain twice as much caloric value per unit of weight as do other foods, until the diet eaten by the top executives of our day contains 55 per cent fat as against the optimum of 20 per cent.[1] Moreover, it has become more and more customary to make the times of our approach to God in missionary conferences and church gatherings into times of feasting instead of times of fasting.

The fact is that amid the intense emotional strains of our day, medical science has pointed out that many people attempt to allay their tensions by eating instead of actually facing a straightforward solution of the problems. Added to this is, as we have pointed out above, the fact that our dietary tendencies provide a definite imbalance of nutrient factors.

While medical science is endeavoring to correct this dietary imbalance, on its own merits, it remains that the Christian should be in the forefront in dealing with emotional problems.

---

[1] These figures represent percentage of calories provided by the fat in the diet.

First of all, emotional tensions should be dealt with by faith in God, not merely allayed through overeating. In the second place, it is our conviction that there are times when fasting as a spiritual exercise has its place. At the same time, we hasten to say that in general we do not believe that this necessarily must be an absolute fast. Many of those who fast as a spiritual exercise do so as a relative and not absolute fast. A prolonged absolute fast lasting much over 24 hours would seem to be dangerous as a rule on medical grounds, in that certain diseases, such as tuberculosis, may well find this an occasion to take hold of the individual concerned.

Let us not be misunderstood on this matter — we are not recommending any ritual whatsoever. We are strongly recommending the exercise of faith in God under all circumstances. This is the essential thing. We have incidentally pointed out that the allaying of emotional tensions through overeating is to be avoided, and that some have found at times that by doing the opposite for short periods of time, they find it easier to deal with basic causative factors of emotional tensions by faith in God.

"Have faith, and doubt not," our Lord Jesus commands.

Chapter 9

DECISIVE LIVING

Wherefore be ye not unwise, but understanding what the will of the Lord is. — EPHESIANS 5:17

AMID THE RAPID SPEED OF LIVING of our modern age there are many who find themselves involved in a veritable whirlpool of activities from which they seemingly cannot extricate themselves. The automobile, airplane, streamliner train, radio, television, and the telephone all make us live more intensively because we are able to have demands made upon us at a greater speed, and in some instances are able to respond to these demands more rapidly. Far less time is left for the art of meditation and thinking, and indeed for some this would seem to be a lost art.

We would not change things so far as modern methods of communication are concerned, for they have brought us great blessing. We would, however, point out that our reaction to these things can be greatly improved.

Feverish activity is not necessarily a measurement of accomplishment, and in many instances it is indicative of little actually being accomplished by a tired, unthinking individual living an unplanned existence. Some indeed revel in the opportunity of showing off some air of importance together with a mild air of irritation at interruption of their seemingly consequential busy career. Well have we been admonished to beware of the barrenness of an over-busy life.

Even Christians try to justify themselves in this sort of thing by pointing out the great number of needy folk they think they are helping, not realizing that Christianity puts more emphasis on quality than quantity. Often have we heard feverishly active Christians trying to justify their way of living by quoting Ephesians 5:16: "Redeeming the time, because the days are evil," as though this meant that they are to rush ahead blindly and feverishly like a chicken with its head cut off.

Their real mistake is that they have removed this verse of Scripture from its context, for the next verse says: "Wherefore be ye not unwise, but understanding what the will of the Lord is" (Eph. 5:17). The implication of these words is clear, and that is that the redemption or buying up of valuable time in these days is to be found in clear discernment of the will of the Lord as to the content, placement, and timing of our service for Him.

The original Greek text for "redeeming the time" presents the imagery of "buying up the opportunity in the market place." Actually entailed in this purchasing is not a random attempt to acquire everything in view, but the selection of what is most appropriate and its acquisition.

We may compare the situation with that of taking little ten-year-old Johnny to the five-and-ten-cent store. Johnny is attracted by the dazzling glitter of everything he sees. His first reaction is that he would like to take everything home with him. The parent realizes full well the folly of such, even if it were financially feasible, for Johnny would become irritated in the extreme over his bewilderment as he faced so many toys. Accordingly the parent helps Johnny to find that toy which is most suited to his temperament and aptitude, and arranges for its purchase. The result is a very delighted boy with a toy which furnishes enjoyment for many days to come.

In like fashion, God leads us as we bring before Him our problem of discerning His will. Many a one, confronted with opportunities for Christian service, reacts at first with a desire to do everything that presents itself without discerning that only certain things are in the Lord's will for each individual. Sometimes we see such individuals going on in such a multiplicity of tasks that they are bewildered in their feverish activity and do not realize that they are accomplishing very little as they drag their tired bodies to and fro to say and do what may prove to be the wrong thing, and that, perchance, at a most inopportune time. Actually all the time their lives are becoming more superficial and artificial, if not a sham, of what they profess to be. Yet these bodies are those which the Holy Spirit had truly wanted to make His temples by dwelling within in all His fullness.

These people often grasp aimlessly at every request that comes to them and every activity that is suggested they engage in until their wearied bodies are in a needless whirl of excitement, and emotional tensions are built up. Often their whirl of excitement expresses itself in a dizziness which is not on an organic basis but represents emotional tensions bombarding the brain as they continue to put forth effort to sustain their activities derived, not from the proper source of bodily energy reserve, but from whipped-up nervous energy which constitutes "living on the nerves."

What a contrast with what we read of Christian service in the Bible! Our Lord Jesus, when He saw that His disciples had become so busied through many coming and going that "they had no leisure so much as to eat," commanded them: "Come ye yourselves apart into a desert place, and rest a while" (Mark 6:31). Many, we fear, acting upon the spirit of our age, would have whipped the disciples up into a renewed fervor of feverish activity, much to the detriment of the quality of their ministry.

Again, we find the Holy Spirit withdrawing Philip from an active ministry in Samaria which had been very fruitful, in order that he might minister to one man, the Ethiopian eunuch, along a desert road as recorded in Acts 8:5-8, 26-40.

The only valid conclusion to be drawn is that what we do is not to be based upon the statistics which we think we can accumulate as evidence of Christian service, but is to be based solely on doing the Lord's will. This involves waiting upon God in prayer but the result is satisfaction in doing what is worth while and represents fruitfulness in the Lord's service. Only with this approach are to be avoided the emotional tensions which build themselves up through indecision and doing too much of what may amount to really very little.

Dwelling in indecision can be especially harmful. Satisfaction is to be found in making a clean-cut decision after prayerful consideration of the issues involved and acting upon it. In our experience the sight of those who have lost out through feverishly attempting to do everything at hand, instead of responding to what seemed to us a clear call from God to a certain service, has been most pathetic. They come to us as medical patients with emotional tension symptoms. By forthright decision in the will of God, these emotional tensions are resolved.

Actually we are confronted with what amounts to a command: "Be ye not unwise, but understanding what the will of the Lord is." This is reinforced by another command also given to us through the apostle Paul: "Prove all things; hold fast that which is good" (I Thess. 5:21).

Even purely on the basis of logic, this is to be justified. Often these individuals say they see so much to be done and no one else to do it, and thus attempt to justify themselves. Yet those who accomplish most under such circumstances do not attempt to do everything they see that needs to be done! For instance, those who administer famine relief in underprivileged lands surrounded by starving millions do not divide their limited supplies of bread among all the millions to prolong the agony of death from starvation for all and thus insure death for all. What they do is to select, usually at random, a certain number of thousands for whom the relief bread is adequate to insure preservation of life. These are given cards and fed day by day throughout the period of famine. In this fashion lives are saved.

Likewise, any physician, once he has passed through a period of internship, during which he went about in a sleepless daze while responding to calls of patients day and night, realizes that the responsibility of being alert to give proper medical care to those in need is so great that he cannot necessarily respond to every call, especially in these days of good telephone service. Accordingly he arranges for some of the calls to go to others who can give just as good medical care while he manages to keep himself in condition to really help those to whom he ministers.

This matter of our daily living being limited to include just those things that are in the Lord's will for us has been very aptly expressed in parable form as follows: "Look at the exquisite fitting in any seed-vessel that you pull to pieces: the seeds are as close as they will go, but fenced off from crowding on each other and hindering each other's growth. He who packed them can be trusted, surely, with the arranging of our lives, that nothing may jostle in them, and nothing be wasted, for we are of more value to Him than these. If our days are a constant rush and hurry, week in and week out, there is grave reason to doubt if it is all God-given seed that we are scattering. He will give us no more to do than can be done with our spirits kept quiet and ready and free before Him."[1]

Another author, writing to fellow Christians in the Armed Forces, puts it this way: "We must not take on more than we can handle effectively and thus risk damaging our entire witness. One of the great tragedies today is that too many Christian officers are doing too much, because so many professing Christian officers are doing too little. There is real danger in being in either group. . . . In order to guard against erring in either extreme, we need to stay close to the Saviour — to save time to fellowship with Him; to study the Word of God and meditate upon it; to listen to Him speak to us through the written Word and learn to discern His guiding hand in circumstances; and above all to spend time talking with Him in prayer. We need to spend time with Him in the Quiet Time — preferably at the start of each day. These are the ways that we can enlist the aid of the Holy Spirit to assist us in maintaining the proper balance in the stewardship of our time."[2]

In this connection it is to be pointed out that a proper admixture of kindness and firmness should be invoked: kindness in accommodating ourselves to others insofar as is reasonably feasible, firmness in boldly refusing to do that

[1]I. Lilias Trotter; *Parables of the Christ-life* (London: Marshall Bros. Ltd).

[2]Edward A. Steele, Jr.; "The Stewardship of Time": *Officers' Christian Union Bulletin*, August, 1955.

which we know we shouldn't do under the circumstances. To this end the middle of our alphabet furnishes two letters which, when used to comprise the word *no,* are of great utility if used kindly and firmly at the proper time, i.e., in accordance with the will of God as it is revealed to us.

These are days for us to make decisions — decisions which narrow us to walking through the strait gate and in the narrow way (Matt. 7:13, 14) but which lead to decisive, fruitful living and service for our Lord and Saviour Jesus Christ.

Chapter 10

FOLLOWING
A SCHEDULE

Let all things be done decently and in order.
— I CORINTHIANS 14:40

DECISIVE LIVING not only has its implications
as regards what we should do, but also as to
when and where we should do it. This involves
following a schedule properly proportioned and
tempered as to content with attention to periods of (1) uninterrupted concentration on
work; (2) complete relaxation; (3) adequate
exercise; and (4) rest in sleep.

We are quite aware that there are those who
insist that they will not be enslaved, as it were,
by a schedule. Actually, such folk eventually
find themselves inextricably in bondage to confusion, frustration, and emotional tensions as
they view what lingers about them undone. A
schedule recognizes that there is only a selection of things that can be done and that these

things are to be done "decently and in order"
in accordance with the scriptural injunction of
I Corinthians 14:40.

It is of interest to note that the confusion or
order, as the case may be, of people's lives is
not purely a matter of mental attitude but is
quite as much a matter of physical arrangement
in one's home and in one's room. Those who
tend to make their desks and rooms into junk
piles are often those who likewise present the
spectacle of confusion in their mental attitudes.
(Incidentally, these folk will most likely profit
greatly from the purchase and use of a sizable
waste paper basket.) Their mental junk piles
produce unnecessary frustrations and emotional
tensions. It is important that this confusion be
avoided at any cost so that the work appointed
may be accomplished.

The most important item in one's schedule
is of course one's work. This at first thought
would seem to be so obvious that it scarcely
bears mentioning. However, the fact is that there
are those who putter away at their work instead
of working at it; that is, they half work and half
relax and really accomplish neither work nor
relaxation. This should not be the case. When
work is being done, full concentration of effort
should be put into it and every moment used
to full advantage. Only in this way is one prepared for the next item on the agenda — com-

plete relaxation after a job well and thoroughly done.

Physiology teaches us that muscles maintain their healthy state through a period of contraction or effort followed by a period of relaxation. The same is true of that aggregate of muscles and nerves, the human body. If there is no let-up in our work, a state of tension develops like the spastic contraction of a muscle in which it becomes inefficient in contracting since its mechanical advantage is lost through failure of previous relaxation. Overfatigue is the result when relaxation does not take place, and this is an essential factor in producing disease symptoms.

Undoubtedly the occurrence of three mealtimes a day makes for just the type of break in one's work that is physiologically suited to bring about relaxation of the entire body. Such times should be utilized in uplifting and cheerful social intercourse and in a manner such as the individual concerned finds most relaxing. The temptation to make mealtime into a time for transacting business should be firmly resisted. Perhaps Christian workers are the more prone to do this since the mealtime sometimes tends to be the most fixed part of the program. This tendency should be avoided since it is provocative of nervous indigestion. Often this can be done through unannounced changes of time and/or place of eating.

Experiments on dogs have shown conclusively that worriment and tormenting of dogs while they are eating is usually followed promptly by vomiting. The delicate mechanism of the human digestion is even more sensitive and must be protected through adequate relaxation. It is much easier to draw the line between work and relaxation when both of them are of the concentrated type and not the puttering type. Relaxation should include relaxation of body, mind, and spirit. For many, actually lying down for 15 or 20 minutes or longer after meals, particularly after the heavy meal of the day, is productive of great refreshment.

Not only should daily periods of relaxation be arranged, but also weekly, monthly, and yearly periods of relaxation. The busier one is, the more important this becomes. While Christians today observe the first day of the week as a special day of worship and devotion and not the seventh day of the week as was customary in Old Testament times, the principle of one day in seven set aside for rest and relaxation is an eternal and a God-given one. In ordaining one day of rest in seven, God said: "Six days shalt thou labor, and do all thy work: but the seventh day is the sabbath of the Lord thy God: *in it thou shalt not do any work*" (Exod. 20:9, 10a).

To neglect to take one day of rest in seven is to invite eventual disaster. Let it not be thought that, since the Sabbath as such has been abrogated, the Christian may work seven days a week with impunity. There must be a laying aside of at least the greater part of a day each week for sheer relaxation. In other words, there should be a scheduled time each week in which no work is scheduled. At such a time the individual should plan on going elsewhere than where he is accustomed to carry on his ordinary work and doing other things such as appeal to him and quite apart from the pressure of a schedule. This may well include a hobby.

Similarly, an annual vacation becomes mandatory. When an individual says he does not feel the need of a vacation, this is almost always a sure sign that he does need a vacation for perchance his feelings have gotten past the sensitive state and have gotten so benumbed that they no longer feel.

In this connection there comes to mind a rescue mission worker in a large city who came to the writer in utter nervous exhaustion. For some ten years he had lived under the conviction that his work was of such importance that no let-up or vacation was to be taken. Wonderful as his work was, he eventually came to the place where he was all tension and could no longer relax; with it the balm of sleep had departed from him. Even though the most modern treatments were used for this man, it was practically a year before he could actively participate full time in his work again. He had learned his lesson, however, and when he went back to his work, it was with planned periods of relaxation. Not only had he foolishly risked his health, but he saw that he had had to spend every bit as much time as he had thought he had saved over the years by not taking vacations, in recovering from his nervous breakdown.

God is not mocked. When His laws are broken, the results are inevitable. The Israelites of old thought in their hearts no doubt that they were being smart in not refraining from their agricultural pursuits every seven years as God had commanded them. They perchance thought they were increasing the amount of grain that was harvested into their barns. This they did over a period of about 490 years only to find in the end that those 70 years, during which time they should have let their land lie fallow, were awaiting them in the captivity of the Jews in Babylon. Full payment was thus made, and that in a humiliating manner. How much better it would have been if over the years they had observed the divine principle of letting the land lie idle one year in seven!

Another important element in the daily schedule is exercise. This should be regular. It should not be characterized by sudden spurts of protracted exertion such as is not indulged in day by day. It should, however, be adequate to keep the body in a state of good muscle tone and nutrition. The type of exercise should be adapted to the individual's bodily needs, particularly with regard to age and physique. With advancing age, particularly beyond 45 years of age, no sudden display of physical prowess should be indulged which goes beyond the type of exercise which has been customary.

Finally, the daily schedule should allow adequate time for rest in sleep. Most people require eight hours sleep each night, and it is wrong for one to try to curtail the sleeping hours merely for the sake of allowing himself to become busier. Indeed, God has given us the darkness of the night seemingly to remind us that that is the normal time to sleep. The healing powers of sleep for a tired body are God-given and are not to be despised. A quiet and rested spirit as an approach to one's daily tasks is even more important than the actual performance of the tasks even as Isaiah proclaimed: "For thus said the Lord God, the Holy One of Israel; in returning and rest shall ye be saved; in quietness and in confidence shall be your strength" (30:15).

Furthermore, if one is confronted with sleeplessness, it is not a sign that the hours in bed at night are to be curtailed but rather is it usually an indication of maladjustment and emotional tension. Often this tendency to sleeplessness is to be overcome through preparing the mind for sleep through relaxation during the hours preceding going to bed. This can best be done through avoiding heavy reading, study, and most of all, one's daily work schedule during this time. The psalmist of old gave expression to this when he said: "It is vain for you to rise up early, to sit up late, to eat the bread of sorrows: for so he giveth his beloved sleep" (Ps. 127:2).

As to the matter of where we are to do our work, this is often more important in the schedule than we at first think. Sometimes through supposed force of circumstances we find an individual attempting to schedule his work, relaxation, exercise, and rest all in the same building, namely, his home. The results of this may be tragic. Relaxation and rest are to be accomplished largely through change of scene from the place of one's accustomed work. The temptation to putter (i.e., to half work and half relax and really accomplish neither) is too great. The work is not done well nor is the remainder of the schedule done well. It is a recognized principle that the best arrangement is to go away from home to an office elsewhere for one's work and to leave one's work there when one comes back home again. It is often surprising the problems that become solved by simply letting them stand idle for a while during which time one's brain can give attention to other things. When the mind is brought back to the matter in question, often there is a ready answer, particularly if the matter has been committed to the Lord in prayer.

Proper attention must be given to forethought in making one's arrangements along the above-mentioned lines. "Let all things be done decently and in order."

Chapter 11

REJOICING IN
THE LORD ALWAYS

*Rejoice in the Lord always: and again I say,
Rejoice.* — PHILIPPIANS 4:4

THE CHRISTIAN IS given a perfect standard by
which he may measure his attainments and according to which by God's power he may model
his life. That standard is the Lord Jesus Christ.

Unfortunately we human beings often lower
our sights. We justify ourselves in stopping
short of our goal in Jesus Christ because we see
others who have done so. We covet the pos-
sessions and dwarfed attainments of others,
when God commands, "Thou shalt not covet,"
and we are willing to stunt our Christian
growth so as to obtain that which we covet. We
see traits and capabilities in others, which we do
not possess, and we become envious of those
who possess these capabilities instead of realizing that each of us has his abilities, and when

one uses them to the full and in the proper manner, he is filling a niche which perchance no one else could fill.

The apostle Paul in his letters to the Corinthian Christians gives us in crystal-clear language the truly Christian viewpoint on these matters. He said: "They measuring themselves by themselves, and comparing themselves among themselves, are not wise" (II Cor. 10:12). There dare be but one standard for the Christian, the Lord Jesus Christ, and we dare not substitute any halfway standard for Him. In so doing we are minimizing God's power and grace, and we are foisting upon the public something which we call Christianity which is not Christianity at all, but a sham.

Christianity is Christ. This standard is attainable by the inworking of God's Spirit within us and by no other means. This implies that God will fit us perfectly into His Body, the Church, in such a way that we fulfill His will and purpose. It does not mean that we are made into perfect speakers, perfect writers, perfect social workers, perfect teachers, and perfect preachers — all in one person. This would be undesirable. Each of us has a niche to fill and each of us is enabled to fill that niche by the power of the Spirit of God.

It is right here that emotional tensions sometimes find their build-up as unfortunate comparisons are made which give rise to needless jealousies. If only we would realize that God does not intend us to be everything all at once! He has a niche for us to fill, and He enables us to fill it.

Thus the apostle Paul tells us that to one is given one gift, to another, another gift (I Cor. 12:8-10), which he summarizes with the words: "But all these worketh that one and the selfsame Spirit, dividing to every man severally as he will" (I Cor. 12:11). Following this it is pointed out that some of us are appointed, as it were, to foot-work, others to hand-work, others to envisioning further developments as an eye, and still others to hearing and doing that which is needed to be done as an ear. When the Spirit of God is allowed to do the appointment and the empowering, there is no room for jealous comparisons. The Spirit's enablings are for specific tasks, and we dare not compare ourselves among ourselves as though it had been by our own strength and power that we had accomplished what we had done; nor should we be discouraged when we see another's accomplishments through the Spirit's enablings in some other line of work from that which we are appointed to do. The Lord has a will and purpose for us, and by His grace we are enabled to do it and nothing else.

Paul illustrates this when he says: "If the foot shall say, Because I am not the hand, I am not of the body; is it therefore not of the body?

And if the ear shall say, Because I am not the eye, I am not of the body; is it therefore not of the body? If the whole body were an eye, where were the hearing? If the whole were hearing, where were the smelling? But now hath God set the members every one of them in the body, as it hath pleased him. . . . And the eye cannot say unto the hand, I have no need of thee: nor again the head to the feet, I have no need of you. Nay, much more those members of the body, which seem to be more feeble, are necessary: and those members of the body, which we think to be less honorable, upon these we bestow more abundant honor; and our uncomely parts have more abundant comeliness" (I Cor. 12:15-18, 21-23).

Actually, the perfection to be seen is not so much in the work each is called upon to do by the power of the Spirit of God as it is in the manner in which each one's task fits perfectly into God's entire scheme of things. In view of this, dare we be discouraged when we see that we are not doing the same things that others are doing? Dare we stop doing what we are appointed to do just because we don't see what we are doing being done by another person, who actually is appointed to do something else?

When we thus view our task, our emotional tensions are dissipated into contentment, and we join the apostle Paul in saying: "I have learned, in whatsoever state I am, therein to be content" (Phil. 4:11, A.S.V.). There is no room for frustration here. We cannot but rejoice that the Lord has thus called us and put us into a job that no one else can do, so important are we to Him in His scheme of things!

Speaking about rejoicing, one of the chief maxims which psychologists give us as a weapon against the emotional tensions of modern living is: "Snap out of your boredom!" To get into boredom the stresses of life have either caused the individual to snap or to slump into it. To get out of boredom requires uplift, and uplift must come from above. It appears to us that "snapping out" and thereby rising above boredom should imply more than just a terrestrial outlook and power.

Actually, in evangelical Christianity we have the perfect answer. The Christian view of life leaves no room for boredom. The Christian recognizes the fact that God is on the throne and that nothing touches his life apart from God's permitting it and even purposing it for him. Each new experience thus is viewed as another unfolding of a new manifestation of God's love, and in this, boredom has no place, but there is a constant rejoicing in the Lord and in His goodness to us.

Let us for a moment consider the way this worked out in the life of Joseph as recorded in the Book of Genesis. Joseph's father, Jacob, as he saw just part of the picture and did not realize that God's good and purposeful plan for him was being carried out, cries out in agony of spirit, "All these things are against me" (Gen. 42:36). Actually, Jacob's viewpoint was what we may call a worm's-eye view in which he saw but a small part of the whole. It is very much like the conclusion of a novice who opens the back of a watch and condemns his watch as no good because he sees one of the wheels turning counterclockwise when he knows that the hands must turn clockwise.

However, Joseph himself, after he had triumphed over his serious difficulty, sees the perfect and purposeful pattern of God's will fulfilled as he takes a bird's-eye view of the whole situation. Joyfully he exclaims: "God did send me before you to preserve life" (Gen. 45:5), and "God meant it unto good" (Gen. 50:20). Joseph did not deny the evil designs of his brothers against him, which thought could have left him to abide forever in frustration and boredom. No doubt it was through rejoicing in the Lord's goodness even amid adversity that his spirit rose above all bitterness over what happened to him, and he eventually saw that nothing had been against him or against his father at all.

Part of our mistake is that we attempt to adjust our mood to the happenings round about us. When these happenings impress us favorably, we may indeed experience some temporary happiness. Happiness, however, in contrast to rejoicing, fundamentally depends upon happenings that seem favorable to us. Happenings are of course beyond our control, and therefore some happenings may soon come our way that may impress us unfavorably. That instant the happiness is gone, and frustration and boredom have replaced it. To live amid such a dependence upon chance happenings does indeed leave us miserable.

However, when we realize that God is on the throne and that "as for God, his way is perfect" (Ps. 18:30), boredom and frustrations are replaced by a perpetual joy in the Lord. This is the Christian's viewpoint if he is at all consistent with his beliefs. No matter what situation may face him, in it he can hear God saying to him as He did to Rehoboam of old, *"This thing is from me"* (I Kings 12:24). He recognizes that there are difficulties to be overcome, but he faces them in the knowledge that the difficulties have been ordered for his discipline and for his growth in Christian grace. He abides in the knowledge "that all things work together for good to them that love God, to them who are the called according to his purpose" (Rom. 8:28).

We, as Christians, should face every situation that comes to us and hear God saying to us in it, "This thing is from me." When we do, we realize that it is just what the Great Physician ordered, and it gives us a balm for the soul. The Christian knows no second-causes.

As Christians we have every reason to be rejoicing in the Lord always as we day by day enter into new and larger experiences of His goodness to us. It is indifference if we are not entering into the fullness of His joy, for our Lord Jesus Himself commands His disciples: "Ask, and ye shall receive, that your joy may be full" (John 16:24). To do this, every care should be turned in prayer. Then, as did David of old, we will say of God: "In thy presence is fullness of joy; at thy right hand there are pleasures forevermore" (Ps. 16:11).

"Count it all joy, my brethren, when ye fall into manifold trials; knowing that the proving of your faith worketh patience," says James (James 1:2, A.S.V., marg.). To do this we simply apply to all situations those words, "This thing is from me," and rejoice in the Lord for His gift to us of one more difficulty to overcome that we may attain to full-grown Christian maturity.

We join the psalmist in saying: "Let all those that seek thee rejoice and be glad in thee: let such as love thy salvation say continually, The Lord be magnified" (Ps. 40:16); and "I will bless the Lord at all times: his praise shall continually be in my mouth" (Ps. 34:1).

Chapter 12

LOVING ONE ANOTHER

By this shall all men know that ye are my disciples, if ye have love one to another. — JOHN 13:35

APART FROM THE WORD concerning rejoicing in the Lord in the previous chapter, our discussion has been based upon considerable introversion and introspection. This has been necessarily the case because our own house must be set in order before we can become effective in extroversion. Nevertheless, the outward uplifting reach is most essential to complete the picture of what God would have us be.

This brings us face to face with what our all-consuming passion as Christians should be. It should be the outward reach toward others which is energized by "the love of God [which] hath been shed abroad in our hearts by the Holy Spirit which was given unto us" (Rom. 5:5, A.S.V.). When the inside of the heart is cleansed of all the hindrances to healthy emotional adjustment, then the heart is ready to receive in all its fullness this love which proceeds from God and makes us love Him and our fellow man more fully.

Selfishness, one of the manifestations of lack of love, can really be a hindrance to right living. The love of God, when filling the heart that has been cleansed of all spiritual contaminants, leaves no room for selfish interests.

It was God's love for the world that sent our Lord and Saviour Jesus Christ into the world to save lost sinners. It is this same love which moves the Christian to go into paths of service to bring those who are out of Christ unto Himself. Thus the apostle Paul says: "For the love of Christ constraineth us; because we thus judge . . . that he died for all, that they which live should not henceforth live unto themselves, but unto him which died for them, and rose again" (II Cor. 5:14, 15).

If the Christian way of life is what we need as individuals to restore emotional balance, and we are convinced that it is, then there is only one conclusion to draw, and that is that it is equally good for the whole world. It is a psychological need of man that he be drawn out of himself. This need is supplied in the great commission given us by our Lord and Saviour Jesus Christ when He said: "Go ye into all the world, and preach the gospel to every creature" (Mark 16:15).

This task which is committed to the Christian is of limitless scope and leaves no possibility of complaint that there is no room remaining for us to move out of ourselves. Moreover, experience proves that there can be no greater exhilaration and uplift for the Christian than to see an individual receive the life of the Spirit through the new birth as the outcome of his witness. This constitutes real fruitfulness in Christian service and gives the same kind of satisfaction that the farmer gets out of a rich harvest.

Love breaks down barriers that no other force on this earth can break down. In this connection there comes to mind an experience that came to the writer when he was a missionary in China during the Sino-Japanese War in 1938. Chinese soldiers had been severely wounded in fighting, and some of their wounded had been carried on stretchers to the mission hospital where he was serving, some seven days' journey over rugged mountains.

Among these was a soldier who had a severe gunshot wound of the right knee. The soldier arrived in severe pain and fever. The knee joint was partially exposed to view, badly infected, and in an indescribable condition. Moreover, there were frequent episodes of profuse bleeding from the knee which left the man in a severely anemic state.

Contacts were made with his military unit for blood donors so that amputation and transfusion could be done. The reply was that there was no blood donor that could be found to give blood to a mere private. Thus it seemed that there was little chance for this soldier to survive.

However, one of the Christian male nurses came to the fore and volunteered to give his blood for the soldier if it proved compatible. It was. The soldier was given the blood and the surgical operation was successfully accomplished.

In the meantime, this soldier had been in our hospital ward. Day by day the evangelist had come to his bedside to tell him about the love of the Lord Jesus Christ, but his ministrations had been spurned.

Not so after the soldier had received the blood transfusion. He had seen and felt the love of God. To think that that male nurse would give his life blood to him, a mere private! He then and there opened his heart to the message of life which the evangelist brought. The act of love of the male nurse was incontrovertible evidence of the truth of the Gospel. The soldier had seen the Lord Jesus Christ in him.

So it is when Christians allow the love of God to have full sway in their hearts, love for others, the real hallmark of Christianity, is manifested.

In doing so, we are fulfilling the psychological necessity of drawing out of ourselves in a way that nothing else in this world can do.

Our Lord Jesus said: *"By this* shall all men know that ye are my disciples, if ye have love one to another"* (John 13:35). Let us let the love of God have full sway in our hearts and lives, loving one another "with a pure heart fervently" (I Peter 1:22). Such love is not conditioned upon the recipient of this love reciprocating the love manifested to him, and therefore it is to be manifested toward all mankind. It is love that is implanted in us by the Holy Spirit, as has been already pointed out. It is love that proceeds from "a pure heart," that is, a heart that has been cleansed of all the contaminants to which reference was made in the preceding chapters. It is furthermore a fervent love which brings before us the picture of something that is not forced out as with a pump but which spontaneously overflows as when boiling takes place with its customary effervescence.

God has commanded us: "Fear not! . . . Forgive! . . . Doubt not! . . . Be not unwise but understanding what the will of the Lord is. . . . Come ye yourselves apart into a desert place, and rest a while. . . . Count it all joy. . . . Rejoice in the Lord always. . . . Love one another with a pure heart fervently." When He commands, He enables. Speaking about God in relation to the inanimate world, we learn from the psalmist: "He spake and it was done; he commanded, and it stood fast" (Ps. 33:9). The disciples, moreover, observed that He commanded even the winds and water, and they obeyed Him (Luke 8:25). How much more is it true of those lives which entrust themselves into His hands that He is able to fulfill His commands in us?

Let no one say it is easier said than done. Such a statement minimizes the power of our Almighty God. It was to a group, who were doubtless saying something similar to this, that is, to the hypocritical Pharisees, that our Lord Jesus addressed His caustic words, "They say and do not" (Matt. 23:3). Let us not be one of a kind with them. God commands and enables us. It is for us to obey.

Having entered into the position of obedience to God's commands, a deep sense of contentment and satisfaction results, knowing that God is responsible for the outcome, and He will not fail. It is in the way of obedience that the heart is cleansed of the contaminants that hinder Christian growth, and every yoke of bondage that would enslave us is broken.

Chapter 13

FAITH HEALING

The prayer of faith shall save the sick, and the Lord shall raise him up. — JAMES 5:15

IN USING THE TERM *faith healing* we are aware that it has many different connotations, particularly among those who would narrow its definition to some specific form of religious rite. Let us rather look at the matter in its broader connotations, for it cannot be denied that there is often a relationship between *faith* and *healing*.

In the first place it is the undisguised purpose of this book to show that, when *faith in God* is allowed full sway, the emotional life of the individual is so brought under control that emotional tensions must go, together with any uncomplicated disease manifestations which they may have produced. As was pointed out, more than 50 per cent of the patients encountered in the average large city medical practice in America are suffering in large measure at least from disease manifestations on an emotional tension basis. Confessedly, at times they are complicated by secondary manifestations of an organic type such as peptic ulcer, which may not yield promptly to that which cures the major cause and manifestations of disease. However, we can say that there is a large percentage of disease symptoms which will disappear when the individual concerned wholeheartedly *puts his faith in God and obeys Him implicitly.*

Alas! How few who profess the name of Christ are willing to go all the way with Him in thus believing and obeying! When they do, however, faith healing of this type of disease is not only possible, it is usually inevitable in the uncomplicated case. This is no physical miracle. It is a spiritual miracle in the sense that God energizes us spiritually, removes our fears, casts out our bitterness and envy, answers our prayers, fills us with His grace, rests our spirits, orders our lives consistently, and makes us overflow with His joy and love. This miracle accomplished, the cure follows along the line of natural law in most cases. In this sense faith healing is to be the expected thing for this type of disease in the individual who sincerely trusts God and obeys Him, and no accompanying fanfare is needed.

Beyond this, we, who believe in the almighty power of God do not deny that He is able to cure *all* disease when such is in His will. God who is the Creator of all nature and the Author of natural law is able to supersede the operation of natural law if He so wills. However, that He does not always see fit to do so, even in response to the wholehearted faith of His children is rather evident, since it is made clear that the apostle Paul himself besought the Lord three times to remove from him his bodily ailment, whatever it was which he called his thorn in the flesh (II Cor. 12:8), and the Lord refused to do so. Instead, He brought untold blessing into his life through the continued operation of the thorn in the flesh. The apostle Paul also informs us, "Trophimus have I left at Miletum sick" (II Tim. 4:20). We see no reason to question the completeness of Paul's faith in God in both of these instances. The conclusion must be drawn that it was not in God's will to give healing in response to this faith in Him in these instances.

On the other hand, many diseases, some of them of even serious nature, such as tuberculosis, are characterized by natural remissions. It is very easy to attribute these apparent cures to faith healing. Sometimes to be sure there may be a coincident faith in God which so acts that the natural remission comes more quickly and is more complete. We merely point out in this connection that *post hoc propter hoc* reasoning (which says, "It came after it, therefore it must have been the cause") cannot be simply applied in these instances without a thorough investigation and evaluation of circumstances by the expert.

Often the exercise of true faith in God leads us to utilize recognized means of effecting a cure. To refuse to do so would be to despise the gifts of antibiotics and other effective medicines which God has graciously put at our disposal through the inventive genius of men who were impelled in many instances to carry on their investigations through distinctively altruistic, humanitarian, and even definitely Christian motives. Healing accomplished through the prayerful use of these medicines, when implicit faith is placed in God to bring about a cure, is no less faith healing than it would be if the cure had been effected by God's working in the individual's body concerned without the use of tangible means.

This calls to mind the experience of Hudson Taylor on his first journey to China as a missionary in 1853. When the sailing vessel in which he was traveling was threatened with disaster, exercised as he was over the situation, he disposed of his swimming-belt thinking at first that this would help him to trust in God more fully. No sooner was this done than he found himself tying a few things in a hamper which he thought would float without any thought of inconsistency or scruple. Later on, aroused to the mistake he had made, he wrote:

"The use of means ought not to lessen our faith in God, and our faith in God ought not to hinder our using whatever means He has given us for the accomplishment of His own purposes. . . . When in medical or surgical charge of any case, I have never thought of neglecting to ask God's guidance and blessing in the use of appropriate means, nor yet of omitting to give thanks for answered prayer and restored health. But to me it would appear as presumptuous and wrong to neglect the use of those measures which He Himself has put within our reach as to neglect to take daily food, and suppose that life and health might be maintained by prayer alone."[1]

The writer is convinced that we can as a rule trust God with greater confidence to bring about healing when we are using recognized healing measures which are at our disposal than when we don't.

This is in line with one of the interpretations which is given to the Scripture passage in James 5:14, 15: "Is any sick among you? let him call for the elders of the church; and let them pray over him, anointing him with oil in the name of the Lord: and the prayer of faith shall save the sick, and the Lord shall raise him

---

[1]Dr. and Mrs. Howard Taylor, *Hudson Taylor in Early Years* (London: Morgan & Scott, Ltd., 1920).

up." This interpretation is to the effect that it
was recognized treatment in the day this was
written to make oily applications to the body
just as we today apply oil of wintergreen for
rheumatic symptoms or ointments to wounds
with good effect. This puts the emphasis rather
upon accompanying the use of recognized
medical treatment with concerted prayer on the
part of the one who administers the treatment,
the patient who receives the treatment, and the
elders of the church. This aspect of treatment
has appealed to me in my practice as a Christian physician as I have prayed with and for
my patients, particularly before operations and
at critical times. The Christian physician definitely has his place as one of the team of two
or three in the fulfillment of the promise given
by our Lord Jesus Christ when He said: "Again
I say unto you, That if two of you shall agree
on earth as touching anything that they shall
ask, it shall be done for them of my Father
which is in heaven. For where two or three are
gathered together in my name, there am I in
the midst of them" (Matt. 18:19, 20).

It is the writer's personal conviction that the
Christian physician can and should have an important place in this prayer-team, and that
whatever healing results is as truly faith healing as any other type of faith healing. Such
would seem to have been the case with Luke,
the beloved physician, as he accompanied the

apostle Paul in later years, evidently prayer-fully ministering to him medically so as to af-ford him relief from his bodily ailment, his so-called thorn in the flesh.

Thus far our discussion of faith healing has been limited to the matter of healing through faith in God. That this is the ideal and most effective form of faith healing is not to be de-nied. At the same time this discussion is per-chance not complete without making reference to two other kinds of faith which may be im-plicated in the healing process: (1) faith in one's physician and in the means he uses to bring about healing; and (2) faith in the spur-ious.

Faith in one's physician is often of great im-portance in bringing about healing. Usually the physician is aware of the fact that he can accomplish nothing in the treatment of the pa-tient without establishing proper rapport. Some-times this requires several visits before confi-dence is built up. Once confidence is estab-lished, the medicine is likely to be taken in the prescribed manner and healing may result. In the absence of confidence often imaginary ad-verse effects of the medicine are complained of and the various incidental moods encountered are blamed upon the treatment with consequent interruptions of therapy.

Many patients seem to be dependent upon explanations in lay language which accord with their own perhaps mistaken and even somewhat weird conceptions of anatomy and physiology, and here often one physician may fail where another succeeds. Certainly, if the patient is unable to change his attitude sufficiently so as to put his faith in his physician in these matters, it is often better that he seek another physician. Faith in one's physician can dispel many fears that are preventing cure, but even so, not as thoroughly are fears thus dispelled as when faith is put in God Himself.

Finally, to make our discussion complete, we point out that faith in the spurious may also actually be responsible for temporarily allaying emotional tensions and effecting relief of symptoms. In this category belong instances where relief is effected by explanations of disease processes which are contrary to the known facts of anatomy, physiology, pathology, or by semblances of technical procedures which may not in reality be of sound value. These may make their appeal to some even though they may be fantastic from the scientific viewpoint and may involve unsubstantiated folklore. In many instances carefully done laboratory tests and X-rays as read by expert X-ray specialists can be utilized to demonstrate that such views and procedures are spurious. Nevertheless, we must admit that faith in such a false statement or spurious procedure is sometimes effective in producing relief of symptoms.

This is no plea for belief in the spurious. We simply are pointing out that faith in whomever or whatever one may see fit to confide often can allay emotional tensions. However, apart from faith in God this relief must frequently be regarded as temporary. Moreover, we do not subscribe to the notion that the end justifies the means, for we believe that it is contrary to God's plan and purpose to utilize any measures which are not in accord with truth and fact. It is our conviction that nothing short of absolute faith in God is adequate to produce the complete relief of emotional tensions which it is God's will for us to experience.

Chapter 14

THE MEANING OF SICKNESS TO THE CHRISTIAN

Most gladly therefore will I rather glory in my infirmities, that the power of Christ may rest upon me. Therefore I take pleasure in infirmities, in reproaches, in necessities, in persecutions, in distresses for Christ's sake: for when I am weak, then am I strong. — II CORINTHIANS 12:9*b*, 10

TO THOSE WHO HAVE ALLOWED emotional tensions to pile up within them to the extent that they have produced disease symptoms, the cure through faith in God is obvious and is readily available. However, it is to be realized that other types of illness afflict the Christian, and it is our purpose in this chapter to discuss what such illness can and should mean to the child of God.

Many a stricken Christian has been puzzled as to why God has permitted sickness to come to him. On occasions there are even those who dare to point the finger of scorn at him, indicating that he must be guilty of some grievous unconfessed sin which has caused his sickness.

The Bible indicates that sickness, suffering, and sorrow exist in the world, as do many other things, because of sin, for we are told that they found their introduction into the world following the sin of Adam and Eve in the garden of Eden (Gen. 3:16-19) and that they sometimes exist because of being bound by the evil one who is the embodiment of sin, as Jesus pointed out when He asked: "Ought not this woman, being a daughter of Abraham, whom Satan hath bound, lo, these eighteen years, be loosed from this bond on the sabbath day?" (Luke 13:16). Nevertheless, it is made clear to us that this is by no means always a direct causal relationship. Sometimes sickness comes to us because of the sin of others. Thus Epaphroditus "for the work of Christ" was nigh unto death because of sinful neglect on the part of the Philippian Christians whose "lack of service" toward Paul had to be supplied by him (Phil. 2:30).

Again, there are times when sickness may be the direct result of hypocrisy in relation to our own unconfessed sin. This may especially be evident in connection with our approach to the Communion Table to pose as partakers of God's grace through Christ. This is pointed out in I Corinthians 11:28-30 where the admonition is given: "Let a man examine himself, and so let him eat of that bread, and drink of that cup," following which the explanation is given that "he that eateth and drinketh unworthily, eateth and drinketh damnation to himself, not discerning the Lord's body." Moreover, it is clearly stated: "For this cause many are weak and sickly among you, and many sleep."

Often, however, the relationship of sin to sickness is remote so that our Lord denied immediate causal relationship with reference to a certain sickness and said that its purpose was that the works of God might be manifested in the sick one (John 9:2, 3). Indeed, the Christian is thereby placed in the unique position of being able to show forth to the world the Christian virtues of patience, longsuffering, joy, and peace in a way that might not otherwise be evident.

But how does it happen that certain ones are singled out for the visitation of bodily affliction upon them? This rather obviously is based upon the eternal sovereign will of our Maker as Paul implies when he asks in Romans 9:20: "Who art thou that repliest against God? Shall the thing formed say to him that formed it, Why hast thou made me thus?" It is, however, also based upon His love, inasmuch as the Scripture says, "For whom the Lord loveth he chasteneth" (Heb. 12:6). Thus we are brought to the position where we see that the visitation of sickness may actually be viewed as a cherished token of God's love, which in its outreaching has singled out the afflicted one as a special object of God's love with a view to being made a partaker of His image, even as the psalmist said: "Before I was afflicted I went astray: but now have I kept thy word" (Ps. 119:67). This is indeed similar to the love of an earthly father which exerts strict discipline even to the point of administering disciplinary affliction toward his very own son when it is needed. "For godly sorrow worketh repentance to salvation not to be repented of: but the sorrow of the world worketh death" (II Cor. 7:10).

One of those who was thus singled out was none other than the apostle Paul. The very man who had brought healing to so many through the power of God was appointed of God to continue in his affliction in order that he might experience more fully the sufficiency of God's grace. Listen to Paul as he tells his experience in II Corinthians 12:7-9a: "And lest I should be exalted above measure through the abundance of the revelations there was given to me a thorn in the flesh, the messenger of Satan to buffet me, lest I should be exalted above measure. For this thing I besought the Lord thrice, that it might depart from me. And he said unto me, My grace is sufficient for thee: for my strength is made perfect in weakness."

It was out of this affliction that Paul was brought to the point where he could actually state in the words quoted at the beginning of this chapter that it was his preference ("rather") to find his delight (or "glory") in his infirmities, and that was not in any morbid sense such as we encounter in the patient who seemingly "enjoys poor health."

In so saying he makes it clear that it was not simply a matter of preference, but that he had made this choice gladly, nay, rather *"most gladly."* Having thus rejoicingly stated his preference, he goes on to assert that this has brought him to the place where the things in which he finds pleasure are directly opposite to those which we might suppose; that is, "in infirmities, in reproaches, in necessities, in persecutions, in distresses for Christ's sake" (II Cor. 12:10). Why? Because it was then that he perceived that the power of Christ was resting upon him and that, although he in his own strength was weak, he was nevertheless finding new strength in the Lord whereby he could say he was now strong.

Dear child of God, if you are afflicted in body, look at this token of God's love and thank Him that He loves you so! Will you not even now seek and find that all-sufficient grace and power that the Lord is waiting to give you, as you take pleasure for Christ's sake in that infirmity which He has permitted to be yours?

Chapter 15

SPIRITUAL GROWTH AND MATURITY

Now unto him that is able to keep you from falling, and to present you faultless before the presence of his glory with exceeding joy, to the only wise God our Saviour, be glory and majesty, dominion and power, both now and ever. Amen. — JUDE 24, 25

WHILE WE ADMIT that the speed and complexity of modern life contributes greatly to the emotional tensions encountered in people of this our day, it remains that the fundamental causes of emotional tension in the human being are the same as those which have been present throughout the ages. The only difference is that we collide with them more often and more forcefully in our daily rounds. Because of his spiritual resources the Christian should not and need not be dragged down emotionally and physically by the burdens and hindrances that drag down the one who is without these resources.

As for the non-Christian we believe that the resources for spiritual victory in Christ are such as to constitute a true challenge to put his faith in Christ and thus enter into the life of the Spirit in which life these resources become available.

Let it not be thought that these potential resources of the Christian are not efficacious just because we come across instances where spiritual contamination in the professing Christian has apparently not been cleared up. We might just as well consider soap and water ineffective in cleansing away dirt since, despite centuries of knowledge concerning their existence and method of use, dirt is still to be found in the world and we don't have to go far to find it! Yet we all know that when soap and water are used, physical dirt is cleansed away. So also may we assure ourselves that when, through the unhindered power of the indwelling Spirit of God, grace, faith, obedience, prayer, praise, rejoicing, and love are consistently applied to the problems of the soul and spirit, spiritual contamination is removed. Then healthy equanimity, and often with it, health itself, spring forth speedily.

It is not our intention to give the reader the

impression that we have given him in these pages a complete treatise on the cure for all diseases. Actually, for the most part, we have limited our discussion to some of the outstanding causes of emotional tensions. Moreover, we have not given a complete compendium of diagnostic criteria of the disease symptoms produced by them. This is because diagnosis is too complicated for the average layman and even experienced physicians may at times be confused at first over the matter of differentiation of these disease symptoms from so-called organic diseases until various laboratory tests have been utilized.

Our aim in these pages has been to stress the importance of the emotional tension diseases and to point out the limitless resources at the disposal of the Christian to eliminate them through maintaining a healthy outlook and thus enhancing his enjoyment and fruitfulness in the service of his God.

Furthermore, it must be pointed out that there are mental diseases, some of them hereditary, the causes of which are entirely beyond the patient's control, although in some instances failure to enter into the fullness of spiritual enjoyment in Christ Jesus may constitute an aggravating factor. The diagnosis and treatment of mental diseases in this category belongs to the expert in mental diseases, the psychiatrist. Moreover, we would add that a Christian should in this instance see a Christian psychiatrist, for we are convinced that the intermingling of pagan philosophy with attempts to extricate the human mind from the entanglements of mental disease is often detrimental to the development of a sound mental state subsequently.

Spiritual health is an asset in eliminating many forms of sickness. However, it does not always assure perfect physical health as we have endeavored to point out in these pages. Many a sickness requires the attention of a physician, and it may even be criminal neglect to await improvement from spiritual adjustments when urgent medical or surgical care is needed. Obviously complete cure cannot be anticipated in all instances. Some illnesses may be designed of our heavenly Father to act like Paul's thorn in the flesh that God's strength may be made perfect in our weakness (II Cor. 12:9). In these instances, relief of suffering rather than cure is to be anticipated, but even here, when our attitude becomes the healthy outlook of Paul, somewhat of a state of health has truly sprung forth!

God, being who He is, deserves to have our wholehearted faith and allegiance in His own right regardless of what benefits may accrue to us physically by rectifying the soul's outlook. The fact that failure to put our trust in Him may cause emotional tension disease symptoms should rather be looked upon as His giving us

gentle reminders that we will be much better
off through heeding His commands rather than
through taking our own way.

The Bible shows us clearly the way that we
should take to become Christlike. Some aspects
of this way have been elaborated in these
pages. The Christian who is satisfied to remain
a born-again spiritual infant is just as pathetic
a sight as the physical infant that never grows.
It is God's purpose for us "to grow in grace,
and in the knowledge of our Lord and Saviour
Jesus Christ" (II Peter 3:18). Only thus can
we attain to that mature "holiness, without
which no man shall see the Lord" (Heb. 12:14).

It is sheer hypocrisy for a person to profess
faith in Jesus Christ and then fail to carry out
the orders of his Lord and Saviour through
which emotional adjustment, that makes for
spiritual maturity, is attained. God gives His
commands with the intention that they will be
obeyed. Moreover, there is no excuse for disobedience since His commands are accompanied by His enablings. Let us give heed to
these commands so that we may grow in Him.
The writer has been frequently impressed with
the speed with which recovery takes place
when the conditions laid down in God's Word
are met. To this end we are commanded:
"Watch ye, stand fast in the faith, quit you like
men, be strong" (I Cor. 16:13).

To God's people in Isaiah's day came the

promise of health on certain conditions. Listen to the list of these conditions in Isaiah 58:6, 7: "Is not this . . . that I have chosen? to loose the bands of wickedness, to undo the heavy burdens, and to let the oppressed go free, and that ye break every yoke? Is it not to deal thy bread to the hungry, and that thou bring the poor that are cast out to thy house? when thou seest the naked, that thou cover him; and that thou hide not thyself from thine own flesh?"

For the purpose of simplification we may take from this the phrase *"break every yoke"* and list the yokes which God's Word informs us are dragging us down. In chapters V to XII we have discussed these yokes together with the scriptural method of breaking them. These yokes that must be broken include fleshly perfectionism, fear, anxiety, worry, resentment, bitterness, an unforgiving spirit, doubt that fails to lay claim to God's promises in believing prayer, indecision, frustration, over-fatigue, covetousness, confusion, jealousy, boredom, and selfishness — all of which represent some form of sin or the consequence of sin. God commands and empowers the Christian to break these yokes. To those who do, there is fulfilled the wonderful promise of Isaiah 58:8: *"Then shall thy light break forth as the morning, and thine HEALTH SHALL SPRING FORTH speedily."*

Moody Press, a ministry of the Moody Bible Institute, is designed for education, evangelization and edification. If we may assist you in knowing more about Christ and the Christian life, please write us without obligation to: Moody Press, c/o MLM, Chicago, Illinois 60610.